About this book

Framework Maths Year 9C has been written specifically for Year 9 of the Framework for Teaching Mathematics. It is aimed at students who are following the Year 9 teaching programme from the Framework and leads to the 5–7 tier of entry in the NC tests.

The authors are experienced teachers and maths consultants, who have been incorporating the Framework approaches into their teaching for many years and so are well qualified to help you successfully meet the Framework objectives.

The books are made up of units based on the medium-term plans that complement the Framework document, thus maintaining the required pitch, pace and progression.

This Homework Book is written to support the Core objectives in Year 9, and is designed to support the use of the Framework Maths 9C Student's Book.

The material is ideal for homework, further work in class and extra practice. It comprises:
- A homework for every lesson, with a focus on problem-solving activities.
- Worked examples as appropriate, so the book is self-contained.
- Past paper SAT questions at the end of each unit, at Level 5 and Level 6 so that you can check students' progress against National Standards.

Problem solving is integrated throughout the material as suggested in the Framework.

Contents

> **Remember:**
>
> ◆ A position-to-term rule links a term to its position (n) in the sequence.
>
> For example, for:
>
> $T(n) = 3n + 1$
>
> $T(1) = 3 \times 1 + 1 = 4$
>
> $T(3) = 3 \times 3 + 1 = 10$

1 Match each of these position-to-term rules with their first five terms.

a	$3n + 5$	**i**	⁻2, 1, 4, 7, 10
b	$5n + 3$	**ii**	2, 7, 12, 17, 22
c	$5n - 3$	**iii**	8, 11, 14, 17, 20
d	$3n - 5$	**iv**	8, 13, 18, 23, 28

2 Here are the first five terms of three linear sequences, all mixed up.

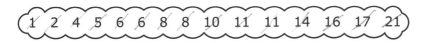

1 2 4 5 6 6 8 8 10 11 11 14 16 17 21

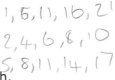

1, 6, 11, 16, 21
2, 4, 6, 8, 10
5, 8, 11, 14, 17

List the three sequences and find a position-to-term rule for each.

5n − 4
2n
3n+2

3 Here are four position-to-term rules:

a $T(n) = 3n$

b $T(n) = 2n - 1$

c $T(n) = 5n - 2$

d $T(n) = 9 + 4n$

Explain in words whether:

i 55 is in each of the sequences.

ii 33 is in each sequence.

Find the value of n for $T(n) = 33$ for each sequence.

1 These are some terms of three different sequences.

a	T(1) = 4	**b**	T(1) = 7	**c**	T(1) = 8
	T(2) = 6		T(2) = 10		T(2) = 12
	T(3) = 8		T(3) = 13		T(3) = 16
	T(6) = 14		T(6) = 22		T(6) = 28
	T(10) = ?		T(10) = ?		T(10) = ?

i For each sequence work out the value of T(10).

ii Which sequence has T(n) = 3n + 4? Explain why this rule works.

iii Find the general term T(n) for the other two sequences.

2 Look at these patterns.

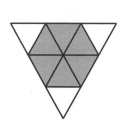 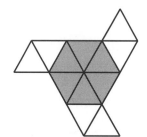 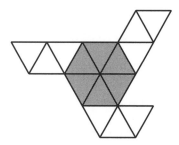

The first pattern is made up of 6 grey tiles and 3 white tiles.

a How many tiles are there in the second, third and fourth patterns?

b A pattern has 6 grey tiles and 45 white tiles. What is the pattern number?

c What is the general rule, T(n), for this pattern?

3 This pattern is in three different sequences.

a It is the first pattern in sequence A
with general term T(n) = 4n + 5.

Draw the second pattern.

b It is the second pattern in sequence B
with general term T(n) = 2n + 5.

Draw the first and third patterns.

c It is the fourth pattern in sequence C.

i Draw the first five patterns in the sequence.

ii What is the general rule, T(n), for sequence C?

> **Remember:**
> A **quadratic** sequence changes by an increasing or decreasing amount. For example: $T(n) = n^2 + 1$ gives a sequence of 2, 5, 10, 17, 26 … The difference increases each time.

1 Here are six sequences.
Which three are quadratic and which three are linear?

a ⁻3, 0, 5, 12, 21   **b** 6, 11, 16, 21, 26   **c** 4, 10, 18, 28, 40

d 4, 9, 16, 25, 36   **e** ⁻2, 1, 4, 7, 10   **f** 16, 14, 12, 10, 8

2 Here are the six general terms, $T(n)$, which match the six sequences in question 1.
Match each general term with each sequence.

a $T(n) = 3n - 5$ e   **b** $T(n) = 5n + 1$ b   **c** $T(n) = 18 - 2n$ f

d $T(n) = n^2 + 3n$ c   **e** $T(n) = n^2 - 4$ a   **f** $T(n) = n^2 + 2n + 1$ d

⑥

3 The table shows the number of diagonals that can be drawn in regular polygons.

Polygon	Triangle	Quadrilateral	Pentagon	Hexagon	Heptagon
Number of sides	3	4	5	6	7
Number of diagonals	0	2	5	9	14

⑦

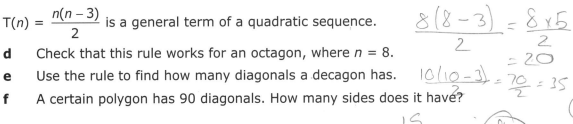

a Copy and complete the table.

b Explain the sequence for the number of diagonals in words. goes up 2, 3, 4, 5… 2nd diff is 1   ①

c How many diagonals would you expect an octagon to have? 20   ①

$T(n) = \dfrac{n(n-3)}{2}$ is a general term of a quadratic sequence.

$\dfrac{8(8-3)}{2} = \dfrac{8 \times 5}{2} = 20$ ①

d Check that this rule works for an octagon, where $n = 8$.

e Use the rule to find how many diagonals a decagon has. $\dfrac{10(10-3)}{2} = \dfrac{70}{2} = 35$ ①

f A certain polygon has 90 diagonals. How many sides does it have? 15   ①

⑱

Level 5

This is a series of patterns with grey and black tiles.

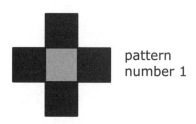

pattern
number 1

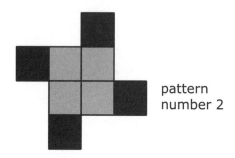

pattern
number 2

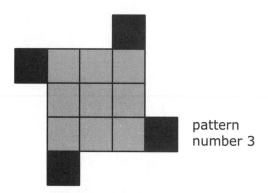

pattern
number 3

a   How many grey tiles and black tiles will there be in
pattern number 8?   *1 mark*

b   How many grey tiles and black tiles will there be in
pattern number 16?   *1 mark*

Level 6

This is a series of patterns with grey and white tiles.

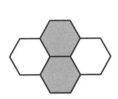

pattern
number
1

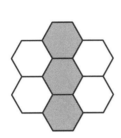

pattern
number
2

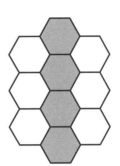

pattern
number
3

The series of patterns continues by adding 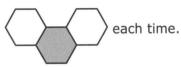 each time.

a Copy and complete this table:

pattern number	number of **grey** tiles	number of **white** tiles
5		
16		

2 marks

b Copy and complete this table by writing **expressions**:

pattern number	expression for the number of **grey** tiles	expression for the number of **white** tiles
n		

2 marks

c Write an expression to show the **total** number of tiles in pattern number *n*. **Simplify** your expression.

1 mark

continued

Level 6

d A different series of patterns is made with tiles.

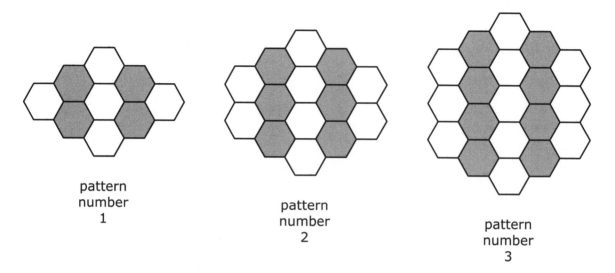

pattern
number
1

pattern
number
2

pattern
number
3

The series of patterns continues by adding [hexagon shape] each time.

For this series of patterns, write an expression to show the **total** number of tiles in pattern number *n*.

Show your working and **simplify** your expression.   *2 marks*

A2.1HW **Revising functions**

1 For this question match the functions with the correct function
machines and the input and output values.

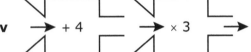

A	$n \to 3n + 4$	**a**	$1 \to 7$ $3 \to 13$ $5 \to 19$

i → × 4 → + 3 →

B	$n \to 4(n + 3)$	**b**	$0 \to 12$ $4 \to 24$ $5 \to 27$

ii → + 3 → × 4 →

C	$n \to 3(n + 4)$	**c**	$^-2 \to 4$ $3 \to 24$ $5 \to 32$

iii → × 3 → + 4 →

D	$n \to 4n + 3$	**d**	$^-5 \to ^-17$ $^-1 \to ^-1$ $2 \to 11$

iv → + 4 → × 3 →

2 For this question it may help to show the functions as function machines.

Here are three functions.

$n \to 5n - 2$

$n \to 5(n - 2)$

$n \to 2n - 5$

a The inverse of one of the functions is $n \to \dfrac{n}{5} + 2$.

Which function is this?

b Find the inverses of the other two functions.

c For the inputs 1, 2 and 3 find the outputs for each function.
Check that these outputs give the correct inputs when you
use the inverse function.

The distance–time graph shows the journeys of three people travelling from Cardiff to Edinburgh, one by plane (——), one by car (- - -) and one by train (…).

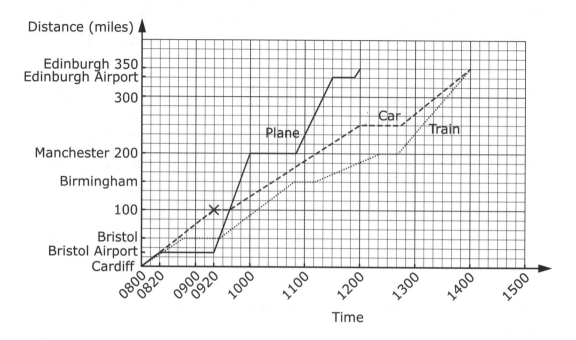

1 What time did the train leave Cardiff?

2 The train passenger changed trains at Bristol.
How long was the wait at Bristol station?

3 Where else did the train stop during its journey to Edinburgh?

4 The plane passenger travelled from Cardiff to Bristol airport by bus. How long did she wait at the airport?

5 Where did the plane passenger change to another flight?

6 Write a description of the car journey.
Describe where the car stopped and how long for.

7 Who arrived in Edinburgh first?

8 What is the average speed for each journey?

9 Which method of transport would you choose for this journey?
Explain your reasons.

$$\text{Average speed} = \frac{\text{Distance}}{\text{Time}}$$

A2.3HW	Interpreting graphs

1 The graph shows the average height for boys from birth to 18 years.

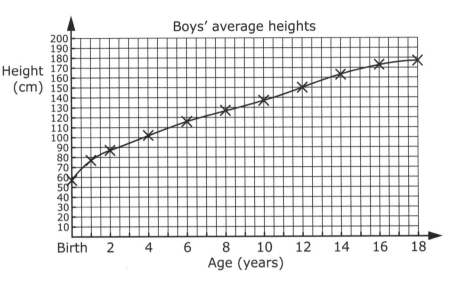

Use the graph to estimate:

a The age of a boy who is 1 m tall

b How many centimetres a boy grows in his first two years

c How tall a boy is at the age of 14

d During which period a boy grows fastest.

2 This table shows the average height for girls from birth to 18 years.

Age	0	1	2	4	6	8	10	12	14	16	18
Height (cm)	50	74	87	101	115	127	139	153	161	163	164

a Draw a graph to show the average height of a girl for her age.

b How tall is a girl at the age of 14?

3 **a** Using the graphs, decide whether you are above, below or average height for your age.

b Compare the girls' and boys' average height graphs. Write a paragraph to explain your conclusions.

Level 5

Some people use yards to measure length.

The diagram shows one way to change yards to metres.

number of yards ── × 36 ⟩ ── × 2.54 ⟩ ── ÷ 100 ⟩ ── number of metres

a   Change **100 yards** to metres.   *1 mark*

b   Change **100 metres** to yards.   *2 marks*

Level 6

Here are five containers:

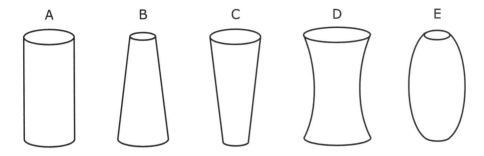

A   B   C   D   E

Water is poured at a constant rate into **three** of the containers.

The graphs show the **depth** of water as the containers fill up.

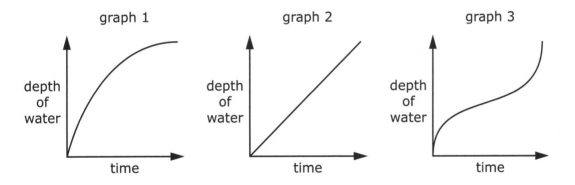

graph 1   graph 2   graph 3

depth of water   time   depth of water   time   depth of water   time

Copy and complete the statements below to show which container matches each graph.

Graph 1 matches container ....

Graph 2 matches container ....

Graph 3 matches container ....   *3 marks*

1 Work out these, giving your answers as mixed numbers where appropriate.

a $\frac{3}{8} + \frac{5}{8}$ **b** $1\frac{3}{7} - \frac{6}{7}$

c $\frac{2}{3} + \frac{4}{9}$ **d** $\frac{7}{8} - \frac{3}{16}$

e $\frac{5}{12} + \frac{1}{16}$ **f** $\frac{15}{16} - \frac{3}{4}$

g $\frac{8}{15} + 1\frac{3}{5}$ **h** $2\frac{5}{9} - \frac{4}{5}$

2 Work out these, giving your answers as mixed numbers where appropriate. The first one is done for you.

a $\frac{5}{9} + \frac{5}{6}$ The LCM of 9 and 6 is 18.

$$\frac{5}{9} = \frac{10}{18} \qquad \frac{5}{6} = \frac{15}{18}$$

$$\frac{10}{18} + \frac{15}{18} = \frac{25}{18} = 1\frac{7}{18}$$

b $\frac{11}{20} - \frac{3}{5}$ **c** $\frac{21}{25} + \frac{9}{20}$ **d** $\frac{17}{18} + \frac{15}{24}$

e $\frac{7}{15} + \frac{^-9}{20}$ **f** $2\frac{9}{10} + \frac{5}{12}$ **g** $3\frac{11}{15} - 1\frac{13}{18}$

3 For each pair of fractions insert >, < or = in between them.
Show your working out clearly for each question.

a $\frac{13}{16} \quad \frac{17}{21}$ **b** $\frac{^-4}{15} \quad \frac{^-9}{35}$

c $\frac{24}{7} \quad 3\frac{4}{9}$ **d** $\frac{17}{28} \quad \frac{37}{60}$

e $\frac{47}{68} \quad \frac{104}{153}$

4 **Investigation**

a Investigate what happens when you work out $1 - \frac{1}{2} - \frac{1}{4} - \frac{1}{8} - \frac{1}{16} \ldots$
Write what you notice.

b Investigate what happens when you work out $1 + \frac{1}{2} + \frac{1}{3} + \frac{1}{4} + \frac{1}{5} \ldots$
Write what you notice.

c Investigate other fraction series:

For example, $1 + \frac{1}{5} + \frac{1}{25} + \frac{1}{125} \ldots$

$$1 - \frac{1}{3} - \frac{1}{9} - \frac{1}{27} \ldots$$

In each case write what you notice.

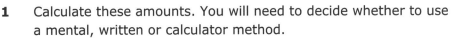

1 Calculate these amounts. You will need to decide whether to use a mental, written or calculator method.
Give your answers to 2 dp where appropriate. The first one is done for you.

a $\frac{3}{4}$ of 22 $\dfrac{3 \times 22}{4} = \dfrac{66}{4} = 16\frac{1}{2}$

b $\frac{3}{5}$ of 175 apples   **c** $\frac{6}{17} \times £70$ **d** $\frac{11}{13} \times 104$ km

e $\frac{7}{8}$ of 140 g   **f** $\frac{11}{3} \times 51$ watts   **g** $3\frac{5}{6}$ of 162 cows

2 Calculate these, giving your answers in their simplest form.
The first one is done for you.

a $\frac{2}{5} \times \frac{3}{4}$ $\dfrac{2 \times 3}{5 \times 4} = \dfrac{6}{20} = \dfrac{3}{10}$

b $\frac{5}{8} \times \frac{4}{7}$ **c** $\frac{10}{3} \times \frac{5}{8}$ **d** $\frac{5}{9} \times \frac{3}{8}$

e $\frac{8}{15} \times \frac{27}{28}$ **f** $\frac{9}{15} \times \frac{10}{21}$ **g** $\frac{8}{35} \times \frac{25}{29}$

3 Calculate these, giving your answers in their simplest form.

a $1\frac{2}{5} \times 1\frac{4}{7}$ **b** $3\frac{2}{7} \times 2\frac{3}{8}$ **c** $2\frac{7}{9} \times \frac{18}{35}$

d $4\frac{4}{15} \times 3\frac{1}{8}$ **e** $\frac{27}{5} \times 1\frac{5}{6}$ **f** $2\frac{7}{18} \times 1\frac{10}{17}$

g $(3\frac{2}{3})^2$ **h** $2\frac{1}{5} \times \frac{45}{44}$

4 **Puzzle**

a Use these clues to work out what fraction of the Multiland flag is light green.

   • The flag of Multiland is in three colours, red, blue and green.

   • For each colour, $\frac{1}{4}$ is in a dark shade and $\frac{3}{4}$ is in a light shade.

   • Overall, $\frac{1}{3}$ of the flag is red and $\frac{2}{5}$ of the remainder of the flag is blue

b Design a version of the Multiland flag which uses the precise fractions of each shade of each colour in **a**.

1   Calculate these, giving your answers as mixed numbers where appropriate.

a $6 \div \frac{2}{3}$ b $14 \div \frac{5}{7}$

c $15 \div \frac{3}{5}$ d $12 \div \frac{3}{4}$

e $7 \div \frac{7}{6}$ f $3 \div \frac{7}{12}$

g $8 \div \frac{4}{7}$ h $11 \div \frac{3}{8}$

i $5 \div \frac{13}{10}$ j $18 \div \frac{27}{100}$

> For example:
> $$3 \div \frac{3}{4} = 3 \times \frac{4}{3}$$
> $$= \frac{3 \times 4}{3}$$
> $$= 4$$

2   Calculate these, giving your answers in their simplest form:

a $\frac{1}{3} \div \frac{1}{4}$ b $\frac{1}{8} \div \frac{1}{10}$

c $\frac{2}{5} \div \frac{3}{4}$ d $\frac{3}{8} \div \frac{5}{7}$

e $\frac{3}{5} \div \frac{7}{8}$ f $\frac{7}{12} \div \frac{5}{4}$

g $\frac{6}{5} \div \frac{8}{15}$ h $\frac{3}{7} \div \frac{14}{9}$

i $1\frac{1}{2} \div \frac{3}{4}$ j $3\frac{1}{5} \div \frac{3}{10}$

k $4\frac{3}{4} \div \frac{7}{8}$ l $2\frac{2}{3} \div \frac{6}{7}$

> For example:
> $$\frac{2}{3} \div \frac{3}{4} = \frac{2}{3} \times \frac{4}{3}$$
> $$= \frac{2 \times 4}{3 \times 3}$$
> $$= \frac{8}{9}$$

3   a   Copy and complete the diagram so that the answer to each calculation is $\frac{3}{7}$.

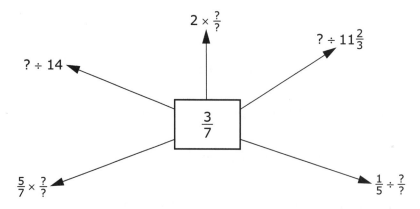

b   Add some more calculations of your own.

1 Calculate these, giving your answers as fractions or decimals
(to 1 dp where appropriate). The first one is done for you.

a 18% of 52 km $\frac{18}{100} \times 52$ km $= 0.18 \times 52$ km $= 9.4$ km (to 1 dp)

b 125% of 40 km   **c** $\frac{3}{7}$ of £9.45   **d** 1.5 of 840 euros

e $3\frac{3}{8} \times 45$ kg   **f** 4.9% of 38 litres   **g** 17.5% of £3405

h $\frac{5}{13}$ of 48 m²   **i** 98.4% of 17 345 km

2 **a** The Big Fat Cat Corporation decides to decrease the prices
of some of its products by 22%. Calculate the new prices of
these three products:

Furry Mice   £2.50
Meow Phone   £11.99
Chocolate rabbits   £4.79

b In a factory for making sherbet lemons, approximately
1.8% of the sweets made cannot be sold and are thrown
away. If the factory makes a batch of 2 482 000 sweets,
how many sweets can they sell?

c Vikram earns £320 per week. His wage is increased by 8%.
Calculate his new wage.

3 **Puzzle**

CLK Bank has two types of savings account.

YEARLY SAVER ACCOUNT
The Yearly Saver account will pay you 3.7% interest on the current balance at the end of each year.
Note: Money can be withdrawn at any time. ·

5-YEAR BOND
The 5-year Bond account will pay you
• 12% interest after 3 years on the initial sum invested
• 3.2% interest on the current balance for each of the remaining 2 years.
Note: Money cannot be withdrawn until the end of the 5-year period.

Albert Schwarzkopf wants to invest £1200.
Which CLK savings account should he choose?

Explain and justify your answer.

1 What fraction of:

a 140 is 75 **b** 5 days is 12 hours **c** 10 kg is 250 g

d £120 is £42 **e** 1800 paper clips is 27 paper clips?

   i Write your answers as fractions expressed in their simplest form.

   ii Write your answers as percentages (to 1 dp where appropriate).

2 Write down the percentage shaded of each shape.

a 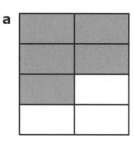 **b** 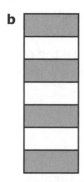 **c** 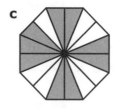 **d**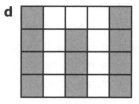

Which shape has the largest fraction shaded?

3 The average number of spectators at FC Lotsofcash
football team's matches increased from 32 000
in 2002 to 34 400 in 2003.
Calculate the percentage increase in the number
of spectators.

$$\% \text{ change} = \frac{\text{change}}{\text{original amount}} \times 100$$

4 **a** Copy and complete this table showing the prices of five items in 1994 and 2004.

Item	Price in 1994	Price in 2004	Percentage change
Season ticket	£190	£370	
Chocolate bar	17p	38p	
Colour TV	£699	£599	
House	£54 000	£124 000	
Car	£10 700	£9 800	

b Which item had the largest percentage change in price?

c Find what the 2004 price of each item would have been if
all the items had changed by:

   i the largest percentage change

   ii 5% a year.

1 a A pair of shoes is on sale for £72, which is 80% of the original price.
What was the original price of the shoes?

Original price = *reduced price* ÷ $\frac{80}{100}$

=£72 ÷ 0.8 = £90

> The first question is done for you.

b Morgan wrote a play called 'The Mystery of Maths' that was
36 400 words long. This was exactly 30% more words than
his editor had asked him to write.
How many words long should the play have been?

c This year Gareth rents a flat for £95.20 per week.
This is an increase of 12% on the rent he had to pay last year.
What was Gareth's rent last year?

d Sue is driving to Preston on the M6 motorway.
She sees a police car in her rear view mirror and reduces
her speed by 3% to 68 mph.
Has Sue been breaking the speed limit of 70 mph?

2 Copy and complete this table showing the length of various films
in their original form and then as the longer 'Director's Edition'.
All times are to the nearest minute.

Film	Original length (min)	Director's Edition (min)	Percentage increase in film length
Lord of the Mathemagical Equations	140	157	
Decimal Point		107	15%
Cubic Wars II	115		19%
The Usual Significant Figures		140	23%

3 Investigation

After a car service, the petrol consumption of Nigella's car
improves by 8% to 37.8 miles per gallon.

The service costs £89. Petrol costs £3.30 a gallon.

a With the improvement in petrol consumption, how much money
will Nigella save on petrol if she drives 5000 miles a year?

b Is the yearly car service good value for money?
Explain and justify your answer.

1 Express each of these as a ratio in its whole number form.
The first one is done for you.

    a   2.5 : 4   2.5 × 2 = 5, 4 × 2 = 8 so 2.5 : 4 = 5 : 8

    b $1\frac{1}{2}$: 5   **c**   3.6 kg : 5.4 kg

    d $2\frac{1}{4}$ m : $1\frac{1}{2}$ m   **e** $2\frac{3}{8}$ km : 4 km

2   **a**   Johnny makes a drink from orange juice and lemonade in
the ratio 3 : 7. How much orange juice will he need to make
500 ml of the drink?

    b   A cake is made with $2\frac{1}{4}$ times as much flour as butter.

         What is the ratio of flour to butter in the cake?
(Express your answer as a ratio in whole number form.)

    c   Mandy is 85% of Tim's height.
What is the ratio of Mandy's height to Tim's height?
(Give your answer as a ratio in whole number form.)

         Mandy is 160 cm tall, how tall is Tim?
(Give your answer to the nearest cm.)

3   The ratio of men to women in two different countries is as follows:

     FOOTLAND   men : women = 7 : 8

     LEGLAND   women : men = 17 : 15

     Which country has the higher proportion of men? Explain and justify your answer.

4   **Investigation**

     The right-angled triangle ABC has angle BCA = 30°.

    a   Draw five different-sized right-angled triangles
with angle BCA = 30°. For each triangle

         i   measure each of the sides a, b and c.

         ii   calculate the ratios $a : b$, $b : c$ and $c : a$.

         Write down what you notice.

         Explain and justify your answer.

    b   Investigate another set of right-angled triangles with angle
BCA = 45°.

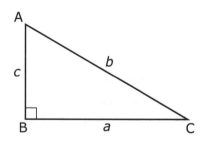

1　Work out the following using mental or written methods.
The first one is started for you.

a　5 tins of lemonade cost 95p.
How much do 13 tins of lemonade cost?

> 1 tin costs $\frac{95}{5}$p = 19p
>
> so 13 tins cost 19p ×13.

b　1 inch is approximately equal to 2.5 cm.
Roughly how many centimetres are equal to 15 inches?
How many inches are equal to 115 cm?

c　A box of 30 calculators costs £53.70.
What is the cost of 10 calculators?
What is the cost of 17 calculators?

2　The numbers in each of these tables are proportional.

a　Copy the tables and write the missing numbers.

i

Number of litres	Number of gallons
27.24	6
	12

ii

Number of oranges	Cost (p)
5	65
18	

iii

Number of jars of jam	Cost (p)
	12.72
25	39.75

iv

Number of kg of cement	Number of kg of sand
13	
8	28

b　Explain how to find each answer using two different methods.

3　Solve each of these problems. In each case clearly show the method you have used.

a　A recipe for leek and Gruyere tart requires 450 g of leeks and 250 g of Gruyere cheese to make enough for 5 people. How much cheese do you need to make enough for 11 people?

b　A pair of shoes is on sale for £80.75, which is 85% of the original price. What was the original price of the shoes?

c　In a recipe for vegetable casserole the weight of potatoes is 175% of the weight of carrots. What is the ratio of weight of carrots to weight of potatoes? What weight of potatoes do you need to make vegetable casserole if you have 4.5 kg of carrots?

1 Solve each of these calculations. You will need to decide whether to use a mental, written or calculator method.
Where appropriate give your answer to 2 dp.

a $^-(5)^2 + 36$

b $(9 - 7)(3 + 4)$

c $(\frac{5}{2})^2$

d $\dfrac{(6 - 2)^2(6 + 3)^2}{36}$

e $\dfrac{(0.6 \times 5)^2}{\sqrt{(8 + {}^-1)}} + 4$

> **Remember:**
> ◆ **B**rackets
> ◆ **P**owers/**I**ndices
> ◆ **M**ultiplication and **D**ivision
> ◆ **A**ddition and **S**ubtraction

2 **i** Write down an approximate answer for each of these questions, clearly showing your method of approximation.

a $\dfrac{72.6 \times 82.8}{4.1 \times (2.4 - 1.9)}$

b $12.27 + (24.5 - (2.3 \times 9.9))$

c $\dfrac{3 \times \sqrt{(4.7^2 + 3.8^2)}}{1.35}$

ii Use your calculator to work out the exact answer, where appropriate giving your answer to 2 dp.

3 **Puzzle**

In Total Countdown you must use all of the numbers given to make the target number. You may add, subtract, multiply or divide the numbers. You may also use any number as a power, and you may use the √ sign.

Remember: Use the order of operations.

a Target number = 5

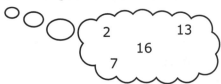

b Target number = 25

c Invent a Countdown question of your own.

Level 5

Screenwash is used to clean car windows.

To use Screenwash you mix it with water.

Winter mixture
Mix **1** part Screenwash with **4** parts water.

Summer mixture
Mix **1** part Screenwash with **9** parts water.

a   In **winter,** how much water should I mix with **150ml of Screenwash**?

1 mark

b   In **summer,** how much Screenwash should I mix with **450ml of water**?

1 mark

c   Is this statement correct?

> **25%** of **winter** mixture is **Screenwash**.

Write Yes or No.

Explain your answer.

1 mark

Level 6

Paul is 14 years old.
His sister is exactly **6 years younger**, so this year she is 8 years old.

This year, the ratio of Paul's age to his sister's age is 14 : 8.
14 : 8 written as simply as possible is **7 : 4**.

a   When Paul is **21**, what will be the ratio of Paul's age to his sister's age?
Write the ratio as simply as possible.   *1 mark*

b   When his sister is **36**, what will be the ratio of Paul's age to his sister's age?
Write the ratio as simply as possible.   *1 mark*

c   Could the ratio of their ages ever be **7 : 7**?
Write Yes or No.

Explain how you know.   *1 mark*

Remember:

The identity symbol ≡ shows that the expressions on either side of the identity **always** have the same value.

1   Identity match

Match each expression in Set 1 with an expression in Set 2.
For example,

$$2x + 3(4x - 2) \equiv 14x - 6$$

Set 1

a $5x + 2(2x - 1)$
b $7x - 3(2x - 2)$
c $4(3x - 1) - 6(x + 1)$
d $(6x - 3) + (3x + 2)$
e $(5x + 7) - (3 - x)$
f $2(5x + 1) - 3(3x - 1)$

Set 2

i $x + 6$
ii $9x - 1$
iii $6x + 4$
iv $x + 5$
v $9x - 2$
vi $6x - 10$

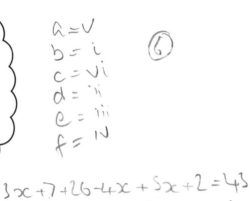

$a = v$
$b = i$
$c = vi$
$d = ii$
$e = iii$
$f = iv$

⑥

2

The perimeter of each triangle is 43 cm.
Write expressions for the perimeters of the triangles.
Use your expressions to find the values of x and y.

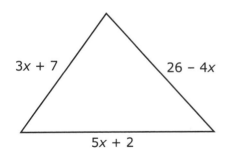

$3x + 7$ $26 - 4x$ $5x + 2$

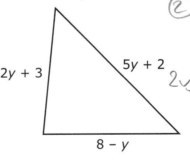

$2y + 3$ $5y + 2$ $8 - y$

$3x + 7 + 26 - 4x + 5x + 2 = 43$
$4x + 35 = 43$
$4x = 43 - 35$
$4x = 8$
$\underline{x = 2}$

②

$2y + 3 + 5y + 2 + 8 - y = 43$
$6y + 13 = 43$
$6y = 30$
$\underline{y = 5}$

3   Simplify each of these expressions:

a $n^8 \times n^2$ n^{10}

b $n^7 \div n^3$ n^4

⑥

c $6(x^2 - 2x)$ $6x^2 - 12x$

d $\dfrac{3a^5}{a^2}$ $3a^3$

e $\dfrac{9p^6}{3p^3}$ $3p^3$

f $\dfrac{12m^5}{4m^3}(2m + m^2)$ $3m^2(2m + m^2$
   $6m^3 + 3m^4$

1 .Match each equation with its solution.

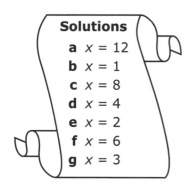

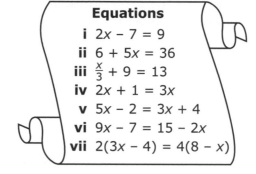

For example, in **i** $2x - 7 = 9 \Rightarrow 2x = 9 + 7 = 16 \Rightarrow x = 16 \div 2 = 8$
So **i** matches to **c** ($x = 8$).

2 For each diagram, form an equation and solve it to
find the missing angles.

> **Hint:**
> ◆ Sum of angles in a triangle = 180°
> ◆ Sum of angles in a quadrilateral = 360°

a

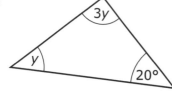

b

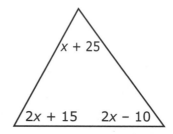

c

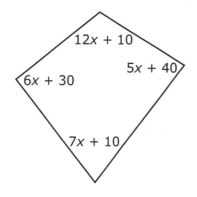

d

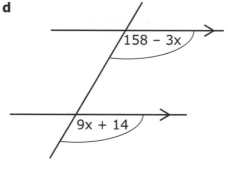

Remember: The square root (√) of a number can be positive or negative.
For example,
$4 \times 4 = 16$ **and** $^-4 \times ^-4 = 16$.
So $\sqrt{16} = 4$ and $^-4$.

1 Calculate these.

    a $3^2 + (^-2)^2$ **b** $5^2 - (^-3)^2$

    c $10^2 - 6^2$ **d** $(^-4)^2 + (^-5)^2$

    e $8^2 - 3^2 + 4^2$ **f** $4^2 - (^-5)^2$

2   **a**   Match the square roots in the inner circle with their values in the outer circle.
Write your answers as: $\sqrt{4} = 2$, for example.

    b   There are two extra numbers in the outer circle.
Write the square of each number.

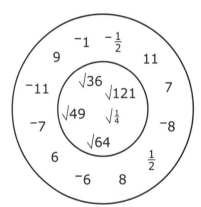

3 Work out the value of x for each square.

    a

x

x	Area = 144 cm²

    b

$x + 2$

$x + 2$	Area = 81 cm²

    c

$x - 3$

$x - 3$	Area = 25 cm²

    d

$x - 7$

$x - 7$	Area = 100 cm²

1   Here are six sizes of photographs.
    Find three pairs that are in direct proportion and find the ratio of
    the width and length for each pair.

a 9 cm / 6 cm

b 12 cm / 9 cm

c 20 cm / 12 cm

d 4 cm / 3 cm

e 12 cm / 8 cm

f 5 cm / 3 cm

2   Solve these equations.

   a $\dfrac{x}{4} = \dfrac{9}{12}$

   b $\dfrac{y}{5} = \dfrac{8}{10}$

   c $\dfrac{z}{3} = \dfrac{12}{8}$

3   Use algebra to find the missing length or width in each rectangle.

    Each pair of rectangles is in direct proportion.

a 24 cm / a / 16 cm / 15 cm

b b / 12 cm / 14 cm / 8 cm

c 7.2 cm / 4.8 cm / c / 6 cm

You will need a calculator.

1 Work out the value of each expression when $x = 2.4$.

a $x^2 + 3x$ b $2x^2 - x$

c $3x^2 - 6$ d $5x^2 - 8x$

e $36 + 2x - x^2$

> For example, for $x^2 + x$:
> $(2.4)^2 + 2.4 = 8.16$

2 For each equation use trial and improvement to find the value of x to 1 dp.

The first one has been started for you.

a $4x^2 - 2x = 101.76$

Estimate	$4x^2$	^-2x	$4x^2 - 2x$	too small or large
$x = 5$				

b $3x^2 - x = 27.56$

c $2x^2 + 7x - 200 = 12.28$

> **Hint:** Use a table for your working.

3 a Write an expression for the perimeter of this rectangle.

b The perimeter is 112.56 cm. Write the perimeter as an equation.

c Use trial and improvement to find the value of x to 1 dp.

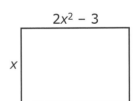

1 Find the value of each of these expressions:

    a $2x^2 - 5x$ when $x = 3.9$

    b $5y^2 + 2y$ when $y = 7.1$

    c $6p^2 - 5p$ when $p = 1.8$

2 Use trial and improvement to find the value of x in these equations to 1 dp.

> **Hint:** Work to 2 dp and then round.

    Complete the tables to help you.

> **Remember:** Use the halfway value to decide how to round a solution.

    a $7x^2 + 2x = 62.5$

x	$7x^2$	$2x$	$7x^2 + 2x$	Too big/ small

    b $3x^2 - 8x = 90$

x	$3x^2$	$8x$	$3x^2 - 8x$	Too big/ small

3 The area of this rectangle is 215 cm².

    Use trial and improvement to find an estimate for the value of x to 1 dp.

    Complete a table to help you.

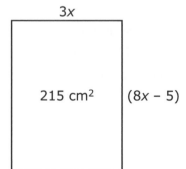

Level 5

Four people play a game with counters.

Each person starts with one or more bags of counters.

Each bag has **m** counters in it.

Lisa   **Ben**   **Cal**   **Fiona**

The table shows what happened during the game.

a   Copy and complete the table to show what **Cal** and **Fiona** had at
the end of the game.

Write each expression **as simply as possible**.

	Start	During game	End of game
Lisa	3 bags	lost 5 counters	$3m - 5$
Ben	2 bags	won 3 counters	$2m + 3$
Cal	1 bag	lost 2 counters	
Fiona	4 bags	won 6 counters, and lost 2 counters	

3 marks

b   At the end of the game, **Lisa** and **Ben** had the **same**
number of counters.
Write an **equation** to show this.   *1 mark*

c   Solve the equation to find **m**, the number of counters in each
bag at the start of the game.   *1 mark*

Level 6

Solve these equations.

Show your working.

1 $8k - 1 = 15$ *1 mark*

2 $2m + 5 = 10$ *1 mark*

3 $3t + 4 = t + 13$ *2 marks*

4 $2(3n + 7) = 8$ *1 mark*

1 Sketch these using appropriate labelling conventions:

a the line AB

b the rectangle ABCD

c the angle ∠ABC

d the parallelogram ABCD with AB = CD

e the triangle ABC with AB extended to D

f the isosceles triangle ABC with ∠BAC = ∠BCA

g the trapezium ABCD where BC is parallel to AD

h the rhombus ABCD

i the isosceles triangle ABC where AC = BC

j the right-angled triangle ABC where C is the right angle

k the kite ABCD where AB = AC.

Remember:

◆ A definition is a set of conditions needed to specify a particular object.

For example, an equilateral triangle is a triangle with three equal sides.

---

2 Write clear definitions of these mathematical terms, using diagrams as appropriate:

a scalene triangle

b rhombus

c kite

d isosceles triangle

e corresponding angles

f vertically opposite angles

g alternate angles.

1   This is a diagram of a pentagon. Use it to copy and complete:

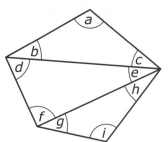

$a + b + c =$ _____

$d + e + f =$ _____

$g + h + i =$ _____

The angle sum of a pentagon is _____.

> **Remember:**
> The angles of a triangle add up to 180°.

2   Find the sum of the interior angles of:

   a   a heptagon (Draw and divide into triangles if necessary.)

   b   a 12-sided polygon

   c   a 24-sided polygon.

> **Hint:** A heptagon has 7 sides.

3   Find the sum of the interior angles of each of these polygons.

   a 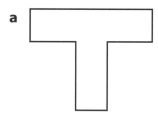   **b** 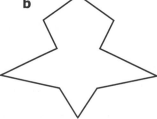   **c**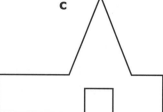

4   This tessellation is made from octagons and squares.

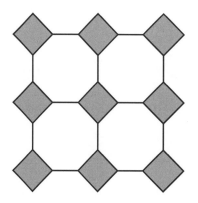

Draw another tessellation that uses two different regular polygons.

Use your knowledge of angles to explain why your tessellation works.

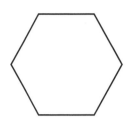

1 Copy and complete these statements.

You can split a regular hexagon into __ triangles.

The sum of the interior angles is __ × 180° = __.

Each interior angle is __ ÷ 6 = __.

Each exterior angle is 180° – __ = __ or $\dfrac{360°}{6}$ = ____

2 Find the sum of the interior angles of each of these polygons.

a    b   c

3 Use your answers to question 2 to work out the interior angle of each of these regular polygons.

    a a regular dodecagon (12 sides)

    b a regular pentagon

    c a regular heptagon (7 sides).

4 Find the exterior angle of:

    a a regular pentagon

    b a regular dodecagon

    c a square.

5 Use your answers to question 4 to find the interior angle of:

    a a regular pentagon

    b a regular dodecagon

    c a square.

Check that your answers for **a** and **b** match your answers to 3**b** and 3**c**.

1 Draw four different shapes with four straight sides.
Mark equal sides and angles.
Name each shape and describe any special properties it has.

2 Find the angles marked with letters in these diagrams.

a

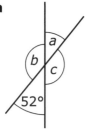

b

Remember:

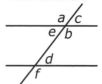

a = b

c = d

e = f

c

d

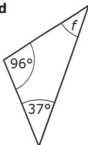

e

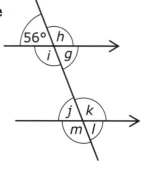

f

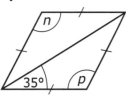

g

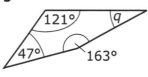

h

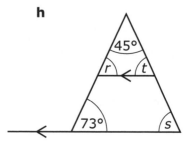

1 Find the angles marked with letters in these diagrams.

a

b

c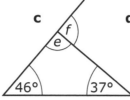

d

2 Find the angles marked with letters in these quadrilaterals.

a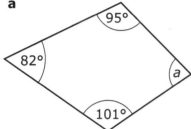

b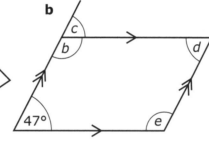

c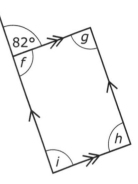

d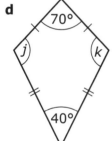

e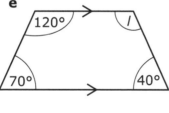

f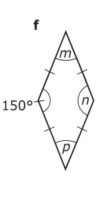

g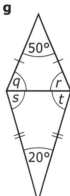

3 ABCD is an isosceles trapezium.

    a Find AB̂C.

    b Find DĈB.

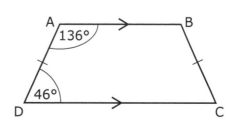

S1.6HW   Circle properties

1   Draw a circle with radius 6 cm.

    a   Label the centre, the diameter and the circumference.

    b   On the same diagram, using a different colour, draw and label:

        i   a sector

        ii   an arc

        iii   a chord

        iv   a segment.

2   Construct this diagram of the sector of a circle accurately.

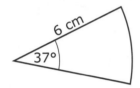

> You will need to use a pair of compasses and an angle measurer.

3   Construct a regular octagon by following these steps:

    a   Work out this angle first.

    b   Draw a circle of radius 6 cm.
        Draw in a radius.

    c   Measure the angle you found in part **a** from the radius.
        Mark the point on the circumference.
        Join the centre to this point.

    d   Repeat part **c** from your new radius.

    e   Repeat again until you return to the start.

    f   You should now be able to draw the octagon.

4   Repeat question **3** for:

    a   an equilateral triangle

    b   a regular nonagon (nine sides).

1 Construct these triangles. Draw your base first, then use your compasses to draw the perpendicular.

a
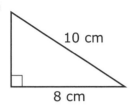
10 cm
8 cm

b
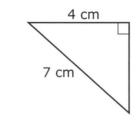
4 cm
7 cm

c
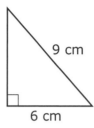
9 cm
6 cm

d
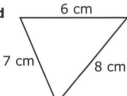
6 cm
7 cm
8 cm

e
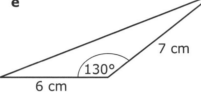
7 cm
130°
6 cm

f
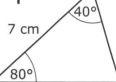
40°
7 cm
80°

2 Construct each of these triangles, if possible.
If not possible, give a reason.

   a ∠A = 60°, ∠B = 80°, ∠C = 40°.

b
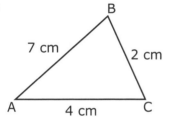
B
7 cm
2 cm
A
4 cm
C

c
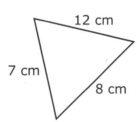
12 cm
7 cm
8 cm

3 The Venetians are raiding Sirmione Castle.

- The castle has an 8 metre moat.
- The Venetians have a 20 metre ladder.
- The castle walls are 16 metres high.

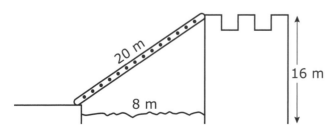

20 m
8 m
16 m

Make a scale drawing to find if the Venetians can reach the top of the castle walls.

1 Kwik Burger delivers within a 5 km radius.
Xpress Burgers deliver within a 4 km radius.
The takeaways are 6 km apart.

Kwik Burger   Xpress Burgers
6 km

Hint: Each delivery area will be a circle.

Draw a scale diagram and label these regions.

a The region which can receive delivery from both Kwik Burger and Xpress Burgers.

b The region which can only receive delivery from Kwik Burger.

c The region which can only receive delivery from Xpress Burgers.

d The region which can't receive delivery from either Kwik Burger or Xpress Burgers.

2 Kwik Burger buys Xpress Burgers and changes the rules.

◆ They both deliver within a 5 km radius.

◆ Houses receive a delivery from the nearest takeaway.

Draw a scale diagram and label these regions.

a The region which receives delivery from Kwik Burger.

b The region which receives delivery from Xpress Burgers.

c The region outside the delivery zone for Kwik Burger or Xpress Burgers.

Hint: The takeaways are 6 km apart.

3 Copy the diagrams and draw the locus of all points that are the same distance from both marked points.

Hint: the locus will be a straight line.

a   **b** 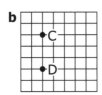   **c** 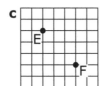   **d**

4 Use a straight edge and compasses to draw the locus of all points that are the same distance from these pairs of points.

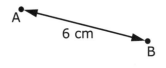   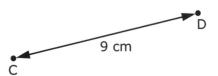

5 A lizard is sleeping on the floor of a hotel balcony.
A mosquito is flying so that it is always 10 cm from the lizard.
Describe the locus of the mosquito.

Remember: The mosquito moves in 3-D space!

1 Copy the diagrams and draw the locus of all points that are the same distance from both lines.

a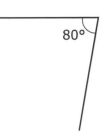

b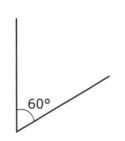

Hint: The locus will be a straight line.

c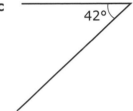

d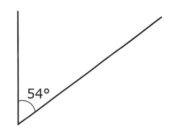

2 **a** Construct a 90° angle using ruler and compasses.

b Bisect the 90° angle using compasses.

3 **a** Construct an equilateral triangle of side 10 cm.

b Bisect each angle.

c What do you notice?

d Repeat for another equilateral triangle.

e Explain what you notice and why it happens.

Level 5

Look at the diagram.
Triangle ABD is the reflection of triangle ABC in the line AB.

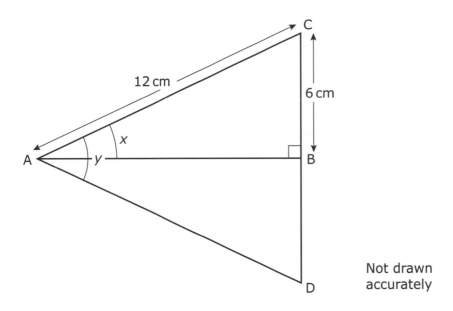

Not drawn
accurately

Copy and complete these statements to explain how to find angle *x*.

The length of AC is 12 cm.

The length of AD is _____ cm.

The length of CD is _____ cm.

ACD is an equilateral triangle because _____   *1 mark*

so angle *y* is _____° because _____   *1 mark*

so angle *x* is _____° because _____   *1 mark*

Level 6

a Any quadrilateral can be split into 2 triangles.

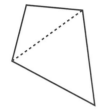

Explain how you know that the angles inside a **quadrilateral** add up to **360**°.

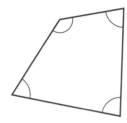

1 mark

b What do the angles inside a **pentagon** add up to?

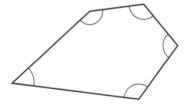

1 mark

c What do the angles inside a **heptagon** (7-sided shape) add up to? Show your working.

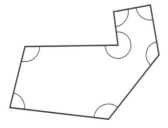

2 marks

The diagram below shows the four stages of the handling data cycle.

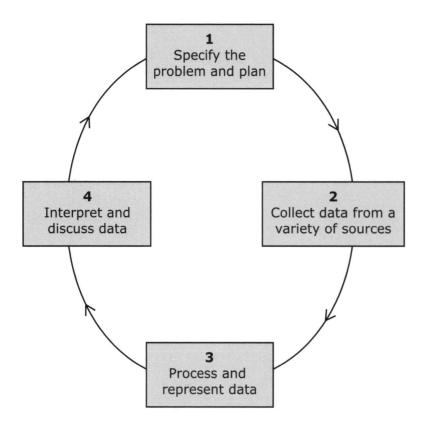

The diagram shows the main stages in a handling data project.

Write a set of 'Hints and Tips' for the handling data cycle.
You should imagine that you are writing some advice for
somebody who has not done handling data project work before.

◆   Use the four stages of the cycle as headings.

◆   Write a paragraph (or a set of bullet points) for each stage,
    explaining some key points about what people should and
    should not do.
    You can include examples and diagrams if you wish.

Aim to answer these questions in your writing:

◆   What are the advantages and disadvantages of a large sample
    size?

◆   Write an example of a useful hypothesis.

◆   How and why would you carry out a pilot survey?

1 The table shows the number of emails that Ken received in one week.

Monday	Tuesday	Wednesday	Thursday	Friday
8	11	15	10	11

Find the mean, median, mode and range of this set of data.

2 Karen records the number of phone calls that she receives each day.

Monday	Tuesday	Wednesday	Thursday	Friday
12	18	22	13	

The table shows the number of calls she received from Monday to Thursday.
She then filled in the number for Friday, and worked out the mean number of calls for all five days.
The mean was 15.
Work out the number of calls she received on Friday.

3 Jo records the number of text messages she receives each day.

Monday	Tuesday	Wednesday	Thursday	Friday
3	7	2	5	

When she has filled in the number of texts she received on Friday, she works out the median and the range.
The range is 9.
What is the median? Explain your reasoning.

4 Write down sets of whole numbers that meet these conditions:

a There are five pieces of data in this set.
The mean is double the median.

b This is a set of six data items.
The mode is equal to the median.

c This data set has seven items.
The median is a lot bigger than the mode, and the mean is a lot bigger than the median.

Here are six different types of diagram that you could use in a handling data project.

a Scatter graph

b Stem-and-leaf diagram

c Time series graph

d Frequency diagram

e Pie chart

f Bar chart

Pick two diagrams.
Give an example of data that you could represent with each type of diagram.

Sketch each diagram and explain the key features that it shows.

1   The pie charts show the results of a survey about journeys to
    school. Children at a secondary school and at a primary school
    were asked how they usually travelled to school each day.

Secondary school

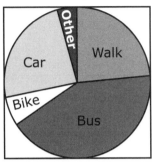

Primary school

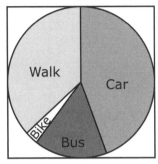

a   Describe the main features of each chart, and the
    differences between the methods of transport used by the
    children at each school.

b   Would it be fair to say, 'There must be more cars arriving
    at the primary school each morning than at the secondary
    school'? Explain your answer.

2   Rita's flat has central heating which is controlled by a timer and
    a thermostat. The graph shows the temperatures inside the flat
    one winter's day.
    Describe the main features of the graph, and explain why you
    think it looks like this.

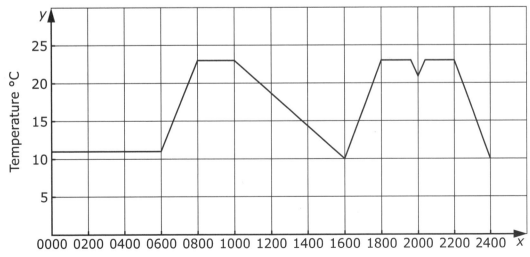

Two classes, 9A and 9B, sat the same Science test, which was marked out of 40.

Their results are shown below.

Test Results for 9A

20	18	26	32	22	23
21	18	26	19	22	23
19	28	14	17	23	21
38	20	23	14	13	19
33	21	20	28	23	19

Test Results for 9B

28	28	30	34	35	27
31	28	34	30	33	30
35	35	29	26	29	32
24	25	31	30	26	30
29	33	29	34	28	36

1   Compare the performance of the two classes in the test.
    You can show the information in diagrams to make this clearer,
    for example, two stem-and-leaf diagrams.

2   Calculate any statistics that help you to compare the two sets
    of scores.
    You could find the mean, median, mode or range.

3   Describe the distribution of the scores for each class.
    Refer to the range of the scores and any other key features.

It is possible to use statistics (like the mean, median, mode and range) and statistical diagrams in a misleading way.
This can be done accidentally or deliberately.

Here are some of the ways in which a misleading impression can be given. You can think about these as a set of 'Dirty Tricks'!

Exaggerate an increase or decrease by adjusting the vertical scale on a graph

Only include some of the data in a chart – leave out the parts that do not support your argument

Change the colour and position of a pie chart sector to make it more prominent

Use a 3-D chart to make the actual data values harder to read

When finding an average, pick the one that supports the impression you want to give

◆ Write a help-sheet to warn people about these techniques, explaining what the effect of the technique is.

◆ Include some examples, so that people know what they should look out for.

The two diagrams show the heights of some girls and boys.

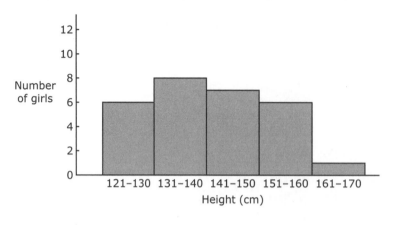

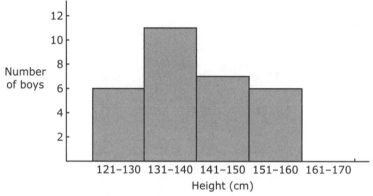

a   Use the diagrams to decide whether these statements are **true** or **false**.
Write True or False.

> There are **more girls** than boys.

Show calculations to explain how you know.   *1 mark*

> The **modal class** for girls is the same as the modal class for boys.

Explain how you know.   *1 mark*

b   The height of the shortest girl is the same as the height of the
shortest boy.
Is the **range** of girls' heights greater than the range of boys' heights?
Write Yes or No.

Explain how you know.   *1 mark*

Level 6

Nine students were discussing their holiday jobs working on a local farm.

They decided to find out if there were any relationships between the time they spent working, sleeping, watching television and the distance they had to travel to work.

The students plotted three scatter graphs.

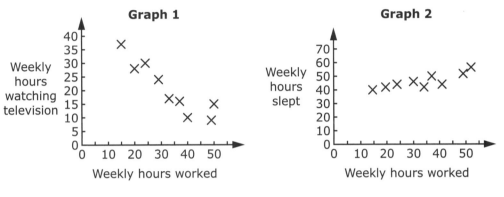

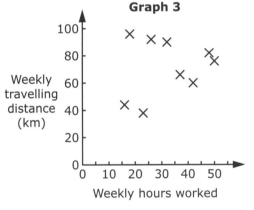

a What does **graph 1** show about the relationship between the weekly hours spent watching television and the weekly hours worked?   *1 mark*

b What does **graph 2** show about the relationship between the weekly hours slept and the weekly hours worked?   *1 mark*

c What does **graph 3** show about the relationship between the weekly travelling distance and the weekly hours worked?   *1 mark*

d Another student works 30 hours per week.

Use **graph 1** to estimate the weekly hours spent watching television by this student.

Explain how you decided on your estimate.   *2 marks*

S2.1HW Measuring area

1 Calculate the areas in cm² of these shapes.

a

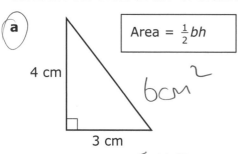

Area = $\frac{1}{2}bh$

4 cm
3 cm

6cm²

b

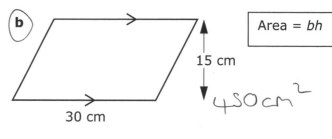

Area = bh

15 cm
30 cm

450cm²

c

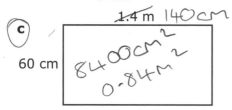

1.4 m 140cm
60 cm

8400cm²
0·84m²

d

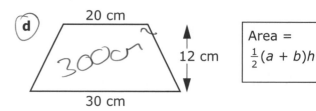

20 cm
12 cm
30 cm

Area = $\frac{1}{2}(a + b)h$

300cm²

2 Change these areas to mm².

  a 8 cm²   **b** 23 cm²   **c** 0.5 cm²   **d** 15.3 cm²   **e** 570 cm²

    800mm²   2300mm²

3 Change these areas to cm².

  a 5 m²   **b** 8.2 m²   **c** 0.73 m²   **d** 18.4 m²   **e** 351 m²

    50 000cm²   82000cm²

4 Change these areas to m².

  a 50 000 cm²   **b** 135 000 cm² 13.5m²   **c** 8000 cm²

     5m²

  d 350 cm²   **e** 8 000 000 cm²

5 Change these areas to cm².

  a 700 mm² 7cm²   **b** 74 mm²   0.74cm²   **c** 8900 mm²

  d 34 mm²   **e** 230 000 mm²

6 Calculate the areas in cm² of these shapes.

a

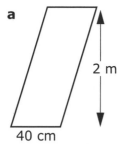

2 m
40 cm

b

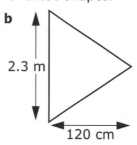

2.3 m
120 cm

c

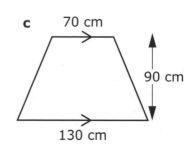

70 cm
90 cm
130 cm

7 Change each of your answers in question 6 to **i** m² **ii** mm².

1 Write down the radius and diameter of each of these circles.

a

12 cm

b 8 cm

c 20 cm

2 Find the circumference of each of these circles.

i Using 3 as an approximation for π.

ii Using the value of π from your calculator.

Circumference = π*d* = 2π*r*

a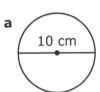

10 cm

b 6 cm

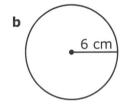

c 19.2 cm

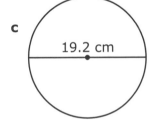

d 3.7 cm

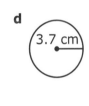

3 The radius of a bicycle wheel is 17 inches.

What is the circumference of the wheel?

4 A Ferris wheel has a diameter of 20 m.

a How far would you travel in one revolution?

b How far would you travel in 20 revolutions?

c A poster says that in one ride you will travel 1 km. How many revolutions is that?

5 **a** The Candy Town Restaurant has a round table with radius 1.4 m.

How many people can sit round the table?

(Assume each person needs 45 cm of space.)

b Eight people sit round a smaller round table.
Find the diameter of this table.

6 Find the perimeter of
each shape.

a

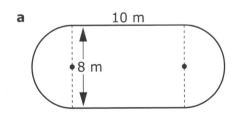

10 m

8 m

b

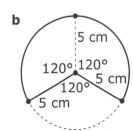

5 cm

120° 120°
5 cm
120°

5 cm

Remember:

Circumference of a circle $= \pi d = 2\pi r$

Area of a circle $= \pi r^2$

1 Find the circumference and the area of each circle.

a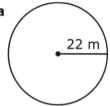
22 m

b
3.2 m

c
48 mm

d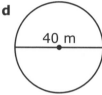
40 m

2 Use π as 3 to estimate the circumference and area of each of these circles.

a
8 cm

b
21 mm

c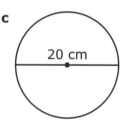
20 cm

3 Find the shaded areas.

a
6 cm

b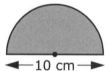
10 cm

c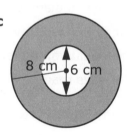
8 cm   6 cm

4 A medium pizza has a radius of 14 cm.

A giant pizza has a radius of 20 cm.

a Find the area of each pizza.

b The medium pizza costs £7. The giant pizza costs £10.
Which is better value and why?

Pizzas come in four sizes: small, medium, large and giant.

c Choose a suitable size and price for a large pizza.
Explain your reasoning.

d Choose a suitable size and price for a small pizza.
Explain your reasoning.

Remember:
- ◆ $C = \pi d$
- ◆ $A = \pi r^2$

1 **a** Find the area of a circle with radius 8 m. ② $201.1 m^2$
   b Find the area of a semicircle with radius 8 m. $100.5 m^2$

2 **a** Find the circumference of a circle with radius 8 m. ② $50.3 m$
   b Find the perimeter of a semicircle with radius 8 m. ② $41.1 m$

3 The radius of a big wheel is 28 m. How far do you travel from the bottom to the top? ① $88 m$

4 Find the shaded areas. **a**

$\frac{254}{28}$ 226.2 mm^2

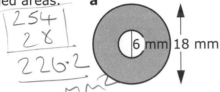

6 mm | 18 mm

b ←12 cm→

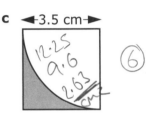

113.1 144 30.9 cm^2

c ←3.5 cm→

12.25 9.6 2.63 cm^2 ⑥

5 This single is made from vinyl.
   The diameter of the record is 18 cm.
   The hole in the middle has a diameter of 0.6 cm.
   a Find the circumference of the record. $56.5 cm$ ③
   b Find the area of the hole. $0.283 cm^2$
   c Find the area of the vinyl. $254.2 cm^2$

6 Gemma designs a birthday card with this shape:
   Find:
   a the area of the front face of the card
   b the perimeter of the front of the card.

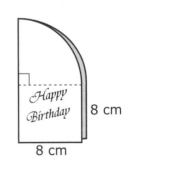

Happy Birthday 8 cm

8 cm

7 Alan has a semicircular pond of radius 2 m
   in his garden. A concrete path 1 m wide surrounds
   the curved edge.
   Find:
   a the surface area of the pond
   b the area of concrete in the path.

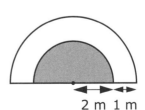

2 m 1 m

1 Calculate the volume of each cuboid in

    i cubic centimetres   **ii** cubic millimetres.

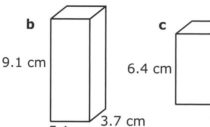
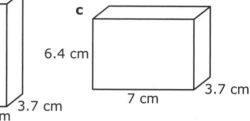

a 5 cm, 6 cm, 10 cm

b 9.1 cm, 5.1 cm, 3.7 cm

c 6.4 cm, 7 cm, 3.7 cm

2 Calculate the volumes of each cuboid in

    i cubic centimetres   **ii** cubic metres.

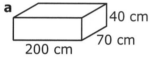
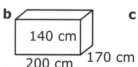
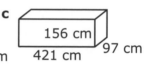

a 40 cm, 70 cm, 200 cm

b 140 cm, 200 cm, 170 cm

c 156 cm, 421 cm, 97 cm

3 Change these volumes to cubic millimetres.

a	5 cm^3		**b**	37 cm^3		**c**	0.4 cm^3
d	270 cm^3		**e**	0.05 cm^3		**f**	15.1 cm^3

4 Change these volumes to cubic centimetres.

a	5 m^3		**b**	0.6 m^3		**c**	7.2 m^3
d	57 m^3		**e**	0.123m^3		**f**	27.9 m^3

5 Change these volumes to cubic centimetres.

a	8000 mm^3		**b**	$270\,000 \text{ mm}^3$		**c**	800 mm^3
d	$75\,000 \text{ mm}^3$		**e**	8 mm^3		**f**	7.5 mm^3

6 Change these volumes to cubic metres.

a	$8\,000\,000 \text{ cm}^3$		**b**	$52\,000\,000 \text{ cm}^3$		**c**	5000 cm^3
d	75 cm^3		**e**	860 cm^3		**f**	8 cm^3

7 Investigation

A container in the shape of a cuboid has a capacity
of 2 litres (2000 cm^3).

Investigate possible dimensions for the container.

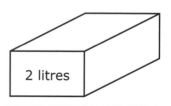

2 litres

Hint:
1 litre = 1000 cm^3

1 Work out the volumes of these cuboids.

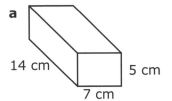

a 14 cm, 5 cm, 7 cm

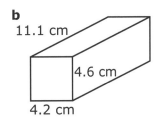

b 11.1 cm, 4.6 cm, 4.2 cm

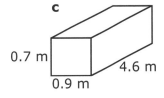

c 0.7 m, 0.9 m, 4.6 m

2 Calculate the surface areas of the cuboids in question 1.

3 Work out the volumes of these prisms.

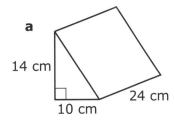

a 14 cm, 10 cm, 24 cm

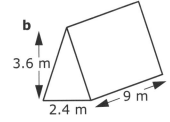

b 3.6 m, 2.4 m, 9 m

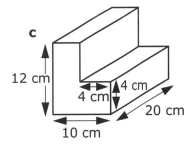

c 12 cm, 4 cm, 4 cm, 10 cm, 20 cm

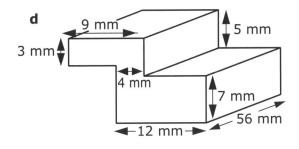

d 9 mm, 5 mm, 3 mm, 4 mm, 7 mm, 12 mm, 56 mm

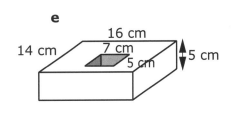

e 16 cm, 7 cm, 14 cm, 5 cm, 5 cm

4 Find the surface areas of the prisms in question 3 parts **a** and **c**.

5 Find the lengths marked with letters.

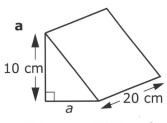

a 10 cm, 20 cm, *a*

Volume = 1000 cm³

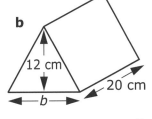

b 12 cm, 20 cm, *b*

Volume = 1200 cm³

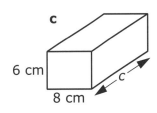

c 6 cm, 8 cm, *c*

Volume = 720 cm³

55

Level 5

This shape is made from four cubes joined together.

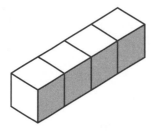

The table shows information about the shape.

Volume	4 cm³
Surface area	18 cm²

The same four cubes are then used to make this new shape.

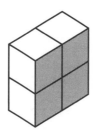

Copy and complete the table for the new shape.

Volume	... cm³
Surface area	... cm³

2 marks

Level 6

A trundle wheel is used to measure distances.

Imran makes a trundle wheel, of **diameter 50 cm**.

a Calculate the **circumference** of Imran's trundle wheel.

  Show your working.   *2 marks*

b Imran uses his trundle wheel to measure the length of the
  school car park.

  His trundle wheel rotates **87 times**.

  What is the **length** of the car park, to the **nearest metre**?

  1 mark

1 Calculate these, using your calculator where necessary.

    a 16^4 **b** 6^{-2}

    c 8^{-3} **d** 24^0

    e 12^5 **f** $\sqrt[3]{42\ 875}$

2 Calculate these, leaving your answer in index form where appropriate.

    a $4^2 \times 4^3$ **b** $5^1 \times 5^2$

    c $3^6 \div 3^2$ **d** $7^4 \div 7^5$

    e $4^3 + 4^8$ **f** $2^4 \times 2^6$

    g $9^3 - 9^2$ **h** $16^7 \div 16^4$

    i $6^2 \times 5^2$ **j** $5^4 \times 5^2 \div 5^7$

> **Remember:**
>
> $5^3 \times 5^4 = 5^{3+4} = 5^7$
>
> $4^2 \div 4^5 = 4^{2-5} = 4^{-3}$

3   **a**   Use a trial and improvement method to find these roots to 2 decimal places.

        i $\sqrt{55}$

        ii $\sqrt[3]{50}$

        iii $\sqrt{500}$

    b   Use the square root and cube root keys on your calculator to check your answers.

4 **Puzzle**

Without using a calculator, find the value of the letters in each of these expressions:

    a $81 = 9^a = b^4$

    b $4^8 = 65\ 536$

          $4^c = 4096$

1 Here are the instructions for a game.

◆ Copy the numbers in Bag A and Bag B.
◆ Choose one number from each bag.
◆ Cross off these numbers.
◆ Multiply or divide them together in your head.
◆ Write your answer and its score.
◆ When there are no numbers left you stop.
◆ Work out how many points you have scored altogether.

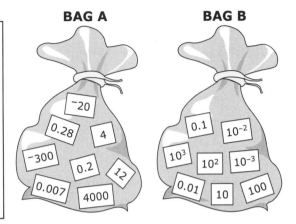

BAG A   BAG B

−20
0.28   4
−300
0.2   12
0.007   4000

0.1   10⁻²
10³   10²   10⁻³
0.01   10   100

SCORES

5 points	**3 points**	**2 points**	**1 point**
$^-0.5 <$ Answer < 0	$25 <$ Answer < 40	$0 \leq$ Answer ≤ 25	Answer ≥ 40 or Answer $\leq {}^-0.5$

Example	$0.007 \times 10^3 = 7$	Score 2 points
	$4000 \div 10 = 400$	Score 1 point

a Write a calculation using numbers from the bags with a score of 3 points.

b Write a calculation with a score of 5 points.

c Write 4 possible calculations (using 4 different numbers from bag A and 4 different numbers from bag B), that would give you a total score of 11 points.

d What is the maximum score you can make using all 16 numbers?

1 Use your calculator to work out these, giving your answers correct to 3 decimal places.

a 19% of 7.5478 m   *1.434 m*

b $\frac{3}{17}$ of 50 kg   *8.824 kg*

c The weight of one baked bean if 277 baked beans weigh 450 g. *1.625 g*

2 Puzzle

Bill receives an invoice from KWIK FOOD UK.

Kwik Food UK	
3 crates of Yorkshire Puddings	£13 197.17

kael delivery.
12 938.40

Bill wants to check the calculation as he feels he may have been overcharged. *weight of 1 bag 5÷3 =1.7kg instead of 3÷5 =0.6kg*

◆ 5 bags of Yorkshire Puddings weighs 3 kg

◆ 1 box contains 24 bags of Yorkshire Puddings   *1 bag = 3/5 = 0.6kg.*

◆ 1 crate contains 18 boxes of Yorkshire Puddings — *432 bags ①*

◆ Yorkshire Puddings cost £5.99 per kg   *1296 bags ②*

Check the calculation using a calculator.   *÷5 = 259.2*

Explain how Kwik Food UK may have overcharged Bill.   *×3 777.6 kg*

£4657.82 real

3 The total land surface area of the Earth is 150 million km².

The approximate land areas of the four largest countries on Earth are:

Russia	17.1 million km²
Canada	9.9 million km²
China	9.6 million km²
USA	9.4 million km²

46/150

Approximately what percentage of the total land surface area of the Earth is contained within these four countries?

30.6 .   *3%.*

1 Calculate each of the following using a mental or written method as appropriate. Try not to use a calculator.

    a   Three angles of a quadrilateral are 146°, 59° and 37°. Calculate the size of the fourth angle.

    b   Three years ago Roger weighed 91.36 kg. Now he weighs 81.7 kg. How much weight has Roger lost?

    c   Katie invests £12 863 into a Share scheme. A year later her investment is only worth 83% of its original value. How much money has Katie lost?

2 Calculate the following using a mental or written method.

    a $2.54 + 6 + 3.9$

    b $23.7 - 5.08 + {}^{-}6.3$

    c $\frac{7}{12} + \frac{8}{10}$

    d $7\frac{7}{8} - 6\frac{7}{10}$

    e $79.2 - {}^{-}47.1 + 3.08$

    f $0.24 + 8.2 + 14 + 7.45$

    g $\frac{9}{5} - 1.53 + 0.68$

3 **Investigation**

These two fractions are made from four different digits.

$$\frac{1}{3} + \frac{4}{6}$$

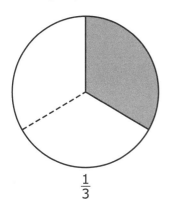 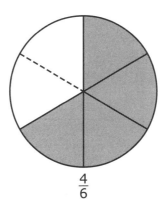

$$\frac{1}{3} \qquad\qquad \frac{4}{6}$$

The sum of the two fractions is 1.

Find as many pairs of fractions as possible, whose sum is 1, which are made from four different digits.

1 Calculate:

a The cost of 21 chocolate bars at £0.45 each.

b The perimeter of a regular 11-sided polygon if each side is 1.84 m long.

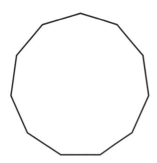

> **Hint:** You could use partitioning as 11 = 10 + 1, so:
> 1.84 m × 11 = (1.84 × 10) + (1.84 × 1)

c The value of 15x if x = 2.9.

d The value of y when x = 3.1 if y = 19x − 14.

2 **a** The entrance fee for a theatre is £12.95 per person. How much does it cost for a party of 49 people to visit the theatre?

b Calculate the number of lengths of wood 0.24 m long that can be cut from a piece of wood 4.08 m long.

3 Give an approximate answer to each of these calculations.

a (3045 × 289) ÷ 60

b 2.75 × (3.36 − 1.41)

c $\dfrac{102.7 \times 0.48}{4.03^2 + 4.2}$

4 Calculate:

a $\frac{3}{4}$ of £54 **b** 15% of £4.84

c Increase 570 km by 60% **d** Decrease 46 mm by 9%

e $\frac{9}{15}$ of £315 **f** $\frac{3}{8} \times 192$

g $\frac{12}{25} \times \frac{15}{16}$ **h** $\frac{12}{25} \div \frac{15}{16}$

Investigation

The number 19 can be split into two parts in lots of different ways.

For example

        10 + 9 = 19

        14 + 5 = 19

> **Hint:** You can also split 19 into 2 decimal numbers.
> For example, 11.5 + 7.5 = 19

The two parts can be multiplied together.

For example

        10 × 9 = 90

        14 × 5 = 70

1   Investigate the different ways that 19 can be split into two parts.
What is the largest product the two parts can have?

> **Remember:**
> ◆ Multiply numbers together to get their **product**.

2   Investigate what happens if 19 is split into three parts.
What is the largest product the three parts can have?

     ? × ? × ?

3   Investigate splitting 19 into four parts … five parts … etc.

     ? × ? × ? × ?

     ? × ? × ? × ? × ?

1   Calculate, giving your answer to 1 dp where appropriate:

    a $18 \div 0.2$ **b** $144 \div 2.4$

    c $735 \div 1.5$ **d** $780 \div 2.6$

    e $240 \div 1.8$ **f** $156 \div 1.1$

2   Calculate, giving your answer to 2 dp where appropriate:

    a $13.9 \div 2.8$ **b** $11.6 \div 0.56$

    c $52.4 \div 0.12$ **d** $0.038 \div 0.0054$

    e $0.669 \div 0.13$ **f** $0.594 \div 6.3$

Puzzle

You can make 100 using exactly four 8s.

For example:

$$\left[\frac{8 + 8 + 8^2}{8}\right]^2 = 100$$

1 **a** What other totals can you make using exactly four 8s?

b Make a set of 20 dominoes, with a question using 8s and an answer to one of your questions on each.

For example:

Question: 8 + 8	Answer: 100

Question $\frac{8^2 + 8}{8}$	Answer: 16

c Play a game of dominoes with someone else.

2 Make the number 1000 using exactly eight 8s.
Can you make it another way?

◆ You must use all eight 8s.

◆ You may use any operations including squares and square roots.

◆ Make sure you write your calculation in the correct order of operations.

Museum

entrance fee

£1.20

per person

a **240 people** paid the entrance fee on Monday.

How much money is that altogether?
Show your working. *2 marks*

b The museum took **£600** in entrance fees on Friday.

How many people paid to visit the museum on Friday?
Show your working. *2 marks*

A drink from a machine cost **55p**.

The table shows the coins that were put into the machine one day.

Coins	Number of coins
50p	31
20p	22
10p	41
5p	59

How many cans of drink were sold that day?

Show your working.   *3 marks*

1   Find all the factor pairs for each of these numbers.

    a   32   **b**   45   **c**   120

2   Copy and complete these prime factor trees.

    a   **b**   **c**

> **Remember:**
> ◆ Break down the factors until they are all prime numbers.

3   Match each number with its prime factors.

    Write your answers as '80 = ...'.

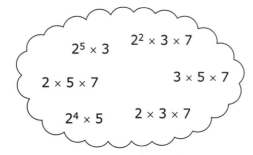

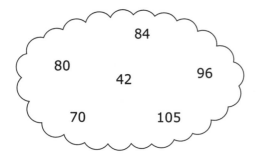

4   Write 204 as a product of its prime factors.

1   Explain in your own words what is meant by:

   a   highest common factor

   b   lowest common multiple.

   Use the numbers 9 and 15 in your explanation.

2   Write down the HCF and LCM for these pairs of numbers.

   a   8 and 20   **b**   15 and 10

   c   18 and 12   **d**   30 and 9

   e   21 and 28

3   **a**   Using the factor tree method, find all the prime factors of 42 and 54.

   b   Use the prime factors to work out

   i   the HCF of 42 and 54

   ii   the LCM of 42 and 54.

4   Factorise these algebraic expressions.
   The first one is started for you.

   a $8xy^2 - 12x^2y$ $=$ $4xy(2y -)$

   b $15x^2 - 10xy$ $=$

   c $4xy - 12y^2$ $=$

   d $3xy^2 + 9y^2$ $=$

   e $14x^2y^2 + 7xy$ $=$

   f $12xy^2 - 3x^2y^2$ $=$

   g $15x^2y + 20xy^3$ $=$

> **Remember:**
> ◆ In 4^3, 4 is the base and 3 is the power.
> ◆ $x^a \times x^b = x^{(a+b)}$
> ◆ $x^a \div x^b = x^{(a-b)}$
> ◆ You can multiply and divide expressions with the same bases.

1 Work out the missing base and power in each of these.

a $2^5 \times 2^3 = \square$ **b** $3^8 \times \square = 3^{10}$

c $5^4 \div 5^2 = \square$ **d** $\square \div 3^4 = 3^2$

e $5^7 \div \square = 5^2$ **f** $\square \times 2^5 = 2^7$

g $\square \div 3^6 = 3^0$ **h** $\square \times 4^3 = 4^7$

i $\square \div 4^3 = 4^7$ **j** $3^4 \div 3^6 = \square$

2 Write each of these as a single power in the form y^n.

a $y^5 \times y^2$ **b** $y^6 \times y^4$ **c** $y^7 \div y^5$ **d** $y^3 \div y^2$

e $y^4 \div y^4$ **f** $y^{-2} \times y^3$ **g** $y^2 \div y^5$ **h** $y^{-3} \div y^{-3}$

3 Write each of these as a single power in the form x^y.

> **Example** $125 = 5^3$

a 49   **b** 144   **c** 1000   **d** 8   **e** 27

f 32   **g** $\frac{1}{4}$ **h** 1   **i** $\frac{1}{16}$ **j** 10 000 000

4 **All wrong**

Here are the results of a five-question test where the answers are all wrong. Explain what you think has been done incorrectly and write down the correct answer.

Q1. $2^3 \times 2^2 = 2^6$ ✗

Q2. $3^2 \times 4^2 = 12^4$ ✗

Q3. $6^3 \div 3^1 = 2^2$ ✗

Q4. $5^{-2} = {}^-10$ ✗

Q5. $4^5 \div 4^{-2} = 4^3$ ✗

1   Work out the value of n in each of these equations.

a $3^4 \times 3^{-2} = 3^n$ b $7^5 \div 7^2 = 7^n$

c $14^8 \div 14^6 = 14^n$ d $2^7 \times 2^2 \div 2^5 = 2^n$

e $11^n \times 11^2 = 11^5$ f $5^3 \div 5^n = 5^5$

2   a   Calculate the values of the terms in this sequence:

6^1 6^2 6^3 6^4 6^5

b   What digit does 6^{10} end in?

c   What digit does 6^{24} end in?

3   a   Calculate the values of the terms in this sequence:

3^1 3^2 3^3 3^4 3^5 3^6 3^7

b   Write down the sequence formed by the last digits of the values.

c   What digit does 3^{15} end in?

d   What digit does 3^{19} end in?

4   Use the number facts in the cloud to find the values of x and y in the equations below.

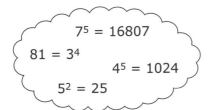

$7^5 = 16807$

$81 = 3^4$

$4^5 = 1024$

$5^2 = 25$

a $3^5 = x$ b $7^y = 2401$ c $125 = 5^y$

d $81 = 3^x = 9^y$ e $4^6 = x$ f $7^5 + 4^x = 17\,063$

5   a   Which of these are square numbers?

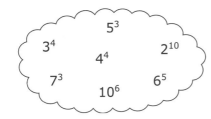

5^3

3^4

4^4

2^{10}

7^3

10^6

6^5

b   Explain how you can tell if a number written in index notation is a square number.

c   Find the square roots of the square numbers you found in **a**, without using a calculator.

Plotting linear graphs

1 **a** Copy and complete these tables of values for the linear functions $y = 4x + 1$ and $y = x - 5$.

x	⁻3	⁻2	⁻1	0	1	2	3
$y = 4x + 1$							

x	⁻3	⁻2	⁻1	0	1	2	3
$y = x - 5$							

b Plot the points on a copy of this coordinate grid.

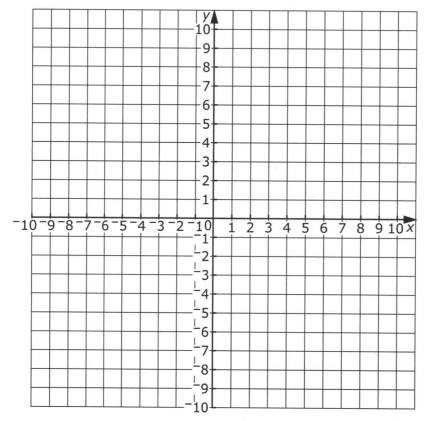

c Write down the coordinates of the point where the lines intersect.

2 **a** Draw up tables of values for these linear functions:
$y = 3x + 1$ $y = 3x + 3$ $y = 3x + 4$

b Plot the graphs of the functions in part **a** on a coordinate grid.

> **Hint:** Copy the grid from question **1b**.

c Where do the lines intersect?
Explain your answer.

d Explain what you can tell about the three lines from their equations.

1 On a coordinate grid similar to this one:

a Plot the points:
($^-$2, $^-$6), ($^-$2, 0), ($^-$1, 8),
(0, 7), (0, 4), (2, 0),
(3, 10), (4, 3).

b The points lie on three different lines with 3 points on each line. Draw in and extend each of these lines and label them A, B and C.

> **Hint:** A point can be on more than one line.

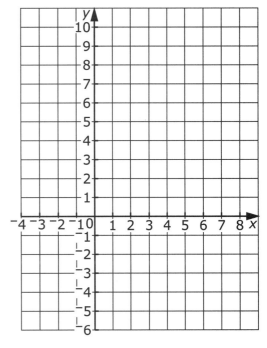

c The equation of one of the lines is $y = 1\frac{1}{2}x - 3$.

Write the equation on the correct line.
Explain using the intercept and gradient why this equation fits the line.

d The line with a negative gradient has equation $y = 7 - x$.
Write it on the correct line.
Explain from your graph how you decide a straight-line graph has a negative gradient.

e For the third line on your graph:

i What is the value of the y-intercept?

ii What is the gradient?

iii Use the gradient and intercept to write down the equation of this line.

2 **a** Copy and complete this table of values for the graph of $y = 5 - 2x$.

x	$^-$3	$^-$2	$^-$1	0	1	2	3
$y = 5 - 2x$			7		3		

b Draw the graph on a coordinate grid. Choose suitable axes.

c Sketch the graph of $y = 2x - 5$ on the same axes.
You may wish to complete a table of values.

d Write down the gradient and y-intercept of each graph.

e Use the gradients and y-intercepts to explain the similarities and differences between the two graphs.

73

1 Rearrange these implicit functions to make *y* the subject of the equation.

a $y - 6x = 4$

b $\dfrac{y}{4} + 2x - 3 = 0$

c $3y + 4x = 12$

d $2y - 6x + 15 = 0$

> For example:
> $y - x = 2$
> $y = 2 + x$

2 **a** Make *y* the subject of these two equations:

    i $y - 2x - 3 = 0$ **ii** $y + 2x - 1 = 0$

  b Write down the gradient and *y*-intercept for the lines in part **a**.

  c Draw the graphs on a coordinate grid, choosing suitable axes.

3 The diagram shows a parallelogram PQRS drawn on a grid.

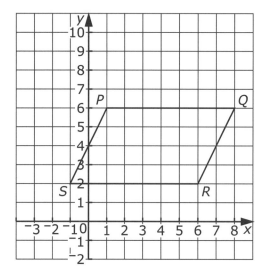

  a Match the correct line to the equations in the box.

| A $y - 6 = 0$ |
| B $5y + 4x - 34 = 0$ |
| C $y - 2x + 10 = 0$ |

    i line through P and Q

    ii line through S and R

    iii line through P and S

    iv line through Q and R

    v line through P and R

  b Work out the equations of the remaining two lines.

1 For each of the situations decide which sketch graph describes it best.

a The distance (y) travelled by a truck moving at constant speed plotted against time (x).

b The temperature (y) of hot water left to cool plotted against time (x).

c The mass (y) of an iceberg as it moves south from the Arctic plotted against time (x).

d The number of litres of fuel (y) left in a car moving at constant speed, plotted against time (x).

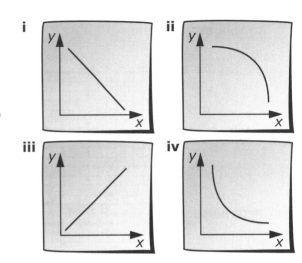

2 This table shows the average temperatures for each month for London.

Month	Jan	Feb	Mar	Apr	May	June	July	Aug	Sept	Oct	Nov	Dec
Temp (°C)	4	4	7	9	12	16	18	17	15	11	7	5

a Plot the information on a copy of this graph and join the points smoothly.

b In which months did the temperature average about 7°C?

c For how long did the temperature average over 10°C?

d There are no months shown with a temperature below freezing point, and yet there were days when the temperature did not rise above freezing. Explain why this is not shown on the graph.

The average temperature for London

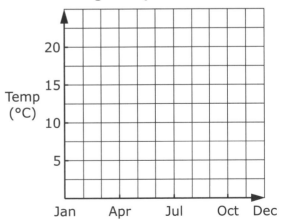

1 This distance–time graph shows the timings for the new London to York express train.

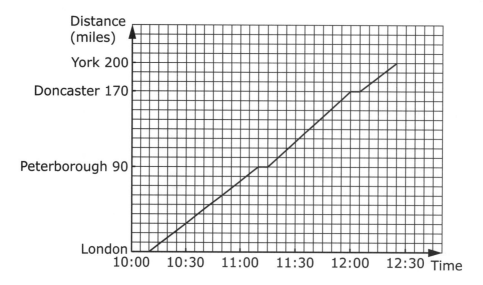

a Copy and complete this table for the arrival and departure times.

London	Peterborough		Doncaster		York
depart	arrive	depart	arrive	depart	arrive
10:10					

b By looking at the times and distances work out the average speeds in miles per hour between:

   i London and Peterborough

   ii Peterborough and Doncaster

   iii Doncaster and York.

c The train continues from York (departs 12:30) to Edinburgh (arrives 14:45) travelling a further distance of 198 miles. What is the average speed for this part of the journey?

d What is the average speed for the whole journey from London to Edinburgh?

> **Hint:** average speed = $\dfrac{\text{total distance}}{\text{total time}}$

a   You pay **£2.40** each time you go swimming.

Copy and complete the table.

Number of swims	0	10	20	30
Total cost (£)	0	24		

1 mark

b   Now show this information on a graph like this one.

Join the points with a straight line.   *2 marks*

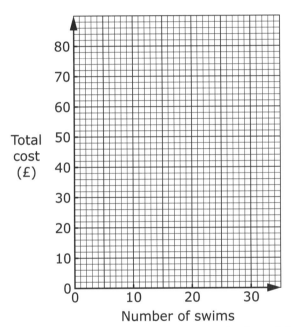

c   A different way of paying is to pay a **yearly** fee of **£22**, and **£1.40** each time you go swimming.

Copy and complete the table.

Number of swims	0	10	20	30
Total cost (£)	22	36		

1 mark

d   Now show this information on the same graph.

Join these points with a straight line.   *2 marks*

e   For **how many swims** does the graph show that the cost is the **same** for both ways of paying?   *1 mark*

Level 6

The graphs shows my journey in a lift.

I got in the lift at floor number 10.

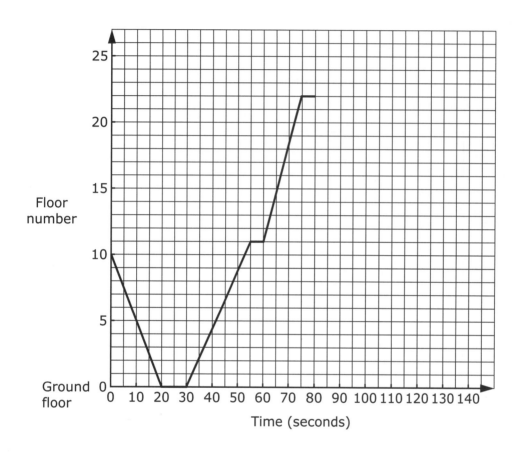

a   The lift stopped at two different floors before I got to floor number 22.

What floors were they?   *1 mark*

b   For how long was I in the lift while it was moving?   *1 mark*

c   After I got out of the lift at floor number 22, the lift went directly to the ground floor.

It took **45 seconds**.

On a copy of the graph, show the journey of the lift from floor 22 to the ground floor.   *1 mark*

1 Draw a diagram of a probability scale from 0 to 1.

  a Mark three different probabilities on the scale, using words and numbers.

  b Write a paragraph to explain how the probability scale works.

2 Sarah has a set of ten digit cards, marked with the digits from 0 to 9. Sarah picks a card at random from the pack.

  a Give an example of an event with three favourable outcomes.

  b Give an example of an event with an even chance of occurring.

  c Give an example of an event with a probability of 0.6.

3 Sam has a pack of five red cards, marked A, B, C, D and E. He also has a set of five blue cards, marked 1, 2, 3, 4 and 5.

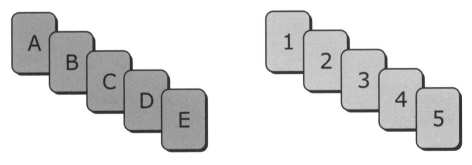

Sam picks a card at random from each pack.

  a Draw a sample space diagram to show all the possible outcomes.

  b Use your sample space diagram to work out the probability of the event 'the red card has a vowel, and the blue card has an even number.'

Remember:

◆ Two events are **mutually exclusive** if they cannot happen together.

◆ The total of the probabilities of all the mutually exclusive outcomes of an experiment is 1.

1 For each of the trials below, explain whether or not the pairs of events given are mutually exclusive.

a An ordinary dice is rolled.

The score is a prime number.	The score is an even number.

b A card is picked at random from a set of digit cards marked 0–9.

The number chosen is more than 5.	The number chosen is less than 7.

c A box contains square blue counters and circular green counters only. A counter is picked at random.

The counter chosen is circular.	The counter chosen is blue.

2 The tables below tell you the scores that can be obtained with some spinners, and the probabilities of each score.
Work out the missing probability for each spinner.

a

Spinner 1	**Score**	1	2	3	4
(4 sides)	**Probability**	0.3	0.3		0.3

b

Spinner 2	**Score**	1	2	3	4	5
(5 sides)	**Probability**	0.1	0.2	0.1	0.2	

c

Spinner 3	**Score**	2	4	6	8	10
(5 sides)	**Probability**	$\frac{1}{5}$	$\frac{1}{10}$	$\frac{1}{5}$		$\frac{2}{5}$

d

Spinner 4	**Score**	5	10	15	20	25	30
(6 sides)	**Probability**	8%		15%	25%	18%	9%

1 **a** Explain how a fraction can be cancelled down to its lowest terms. Give some examples.

b Show how cancelling a fraction can help you to solve the problem below.

There are 40 marbles in a jar, and 36 of them are green. When a marble is chosen at random, what is the probability of it being green?

2 **a** Explain how fractions can be added and subtracted. Give some examples.

b A spinner has sections labelled A, B, C and D. The probability of getting A is $\frac{1}{4}$, and the probability of getting B is $\frac{1}{5}$.

What is the total of the probabilities of A and B?

c The probability of winning a game is $\frac{2}{7}$.
What is the probability of not winning?

3 **a** Explain how multiplying a fraction by a whole number can help you to work out the expected number of successes when an experiment is repeated. Give an example.

b The probability of winning a game is $\frac{3}{5}$.
How many wins would you expect if you played the game 100 times?

Write an instruction sheet explaining how to estimate an experimental probability.

You should give an example of an experiment, and explain:

◆ How to carry out the experiment.

◆ How to record the results.

◆ How to calculate the estimated probabilities.

◆ How to make the estimated probabilities more accurate.

> **Remember:**
>
> Experimental probability =
> $$\frac{\text{number of successful trials}}{\text{total number of trials}}$$

Here is some apparatus you could use:

Level 5

In each box of cereal there is a free gift of a card.
You cannot tell which card will be in a box.
Each card is equally likely.

There are **four** different cards: A, B, C or D

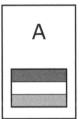 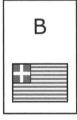 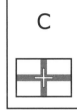 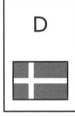

a   **Zoe** needs card **A**.
    Her brother **Paul** needs cards **C** and **D**.

    They buy one box of cereal.

    What is the probability that the card is one that **Zoe** needs?   *1 mark*

    What is the probability that the card is one that **Paul** needs?
                                                                        1 mark

b   Then their mother opens the box.
    She tells them the card is **not card A**.

    Now what is the probability the card is one that **Zoe** needs?
                                                                        1 mark

    What is the probability that the card is one that **Paul** needs?
                                                                        1 mark

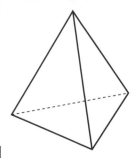

Level 6

This dice with 4 faces has one blue, one green, one red and one yellow face.

Five pupils did an experiment to investigate whether the dice was biased or not.

The data they collected are shown in this table.

Pupil's Name	Number of throws	Face landed on			
		Red	Blue	Green	Yellow
Peter	20	9	7	2	2
Caryl	60	23	20	8	9
Shana	250	85	90	36	39
Keith	40	15	15	6	4
Paul	150	47	54	23	26

a Which pupil's data is **most likely** to give the best estimate of the probability of getting each colour on the dice?

Explain your answer.   *1 mark*

The pupils collected all the data together.

Number of throws	Face landed on			
	Red	Blue	Green	Yellow
520	179	186	75	80

b Consider the data.

Write down whether you think the dice is biased or unbiased, and explain your answer.   *1 mark*

c From the data work out the probability of the dice landing on the blue face.   *1 mark*

d From the data work out the probability of the dice landing on the green face.   *1 mark*

1   On a copy of this grid reflect the triangle T in:

   a   the *x*-axis and label the image A

   b   the *y*-axis and label the image B

   c   the line *x* = ⁻2 and label the image C

   d   the line *y* = 2 and label the image D.

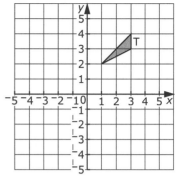

2   On separate copies of this diagram draw the image of the triangle T, after these rotations:

   a   90° clockwise about (1, 1)

   b   a half-turn about (0, 0)

   c   a half-turn about (3, 2)

   d   90° anticlockwise about (0, 0).

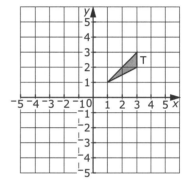

3   **a**   Copy the diagram.

      i   Reflect triangle A in the *y*-axis and label the image B.

      ii   Reflect triangle A in the *x*-axis and label the image C.

   b   Copy the diagram again.

      i   Rotate triangle A 90° clockwise, centre (0, 0), and label the image P.

      ii   Rotate triangle A 90° anticlockwise, centre (0, 0), and label the image Q.

      iii Rotate triangle A by a half-turn, centre (0, 0), and label the image R.

      iv   What rotation transforms triangle Q to triangle P?

   c   Copy the diagram again.

      i   Translate triangle A using the vector $\begin{pmatrix} -5 \\ 2 \end{pmatrix}$ and label the image X.

      ii   Translate triangle A using the vector $\begin{pmatrix} -2 \\ -5 \end{pmatrix}$ and label the image Y.

      iii What translation will move triangle X to triangle Y?

      iv   What translation will move triangle Y back to triangle A?

1 Copy the diagram and draw these transformations of the shape A:

   a Reflection in $y = 2$ (label the image B)

   b Reflection in $x = 2$ (label the image C)

   c Reflection in $x = {}^-2$ (label the image D)

   d Reflection in $y = 4$ (label the image E).

On a separate copy of the diagram draw these transformations of shape A:

   e 90° clockwise rotation about (0, 0) (label the image F)

   f Half-turn rotation about (0, 0) (label the image G)

   g 90° anticlockwise rotation, centre (0, 3) (label the image H)

   h Translation with vector $\begin{pmatrix} {}^-4 \\ {}^-6 \end{pmatrix}$ (label the image I)

   i Translation with vector $\begin{pmatrix} 3 \\ {}^-4 \end{pmatrix}$ (label the image J).

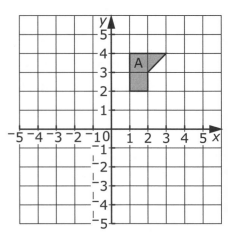

2 The diagram shows eight congruent triangles labelled A to H.

Describe these transformations.

   a Triangle A to triangle B

   b Triangle B to triangle A

   c Triangle A to triangle D

   d Triangle A to triangle F

   e Triangle A to triangle E

   f Triangle D to triangle E

   g Triangle G to triangle A

   h Triangle G to triangle H.

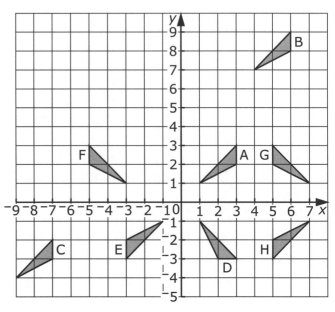

1 Copy the diagram.

   a Reflect triangle A in the *x*-axis and label the image A'.

   b Reflect triangle A' in the *y*-axis and label the image A''.

   c What single transformation will transform triangle A to triangle A''?

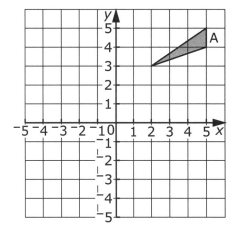

2 Repeat question 1 but change the order of the reflections.

   What do you notice?

3 Investigate combinations of:

   ◆ reflections, for example the effect of a reflection in *x* = 4, followed by a reflection in *y* = 4

   ◆ rotations

   ◆ translations.

   Give at least two examples for each with diagrams and justify any conclusions.

4 Describe these transformations, or combinations of transformations:

   a A to B

   b B to C

   c the **single** transformation A to D

   d D to E

   e D to F

   f A to F

   g D to G

   h A to G

   i G to H.

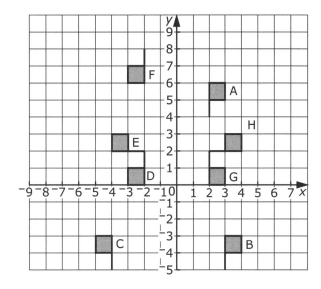

1 Make sketches to show the planes of symmetry of these solids.

a

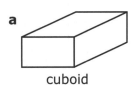

cuboid

b

(right-angled) triangular prism

> A plane of symmetry divides the shape into identical parts.

c

cylinder

d

pentagonal prism

e

hexagonal prism

f

cone

2 A cube has nine planes of symmetry.

Use sketches to show them all.

3 Can you slice a regular square-based pyramid so that the cross-section is:

a a square

b an isosceles triangle

c a trapezium

d an equilateral triangle?

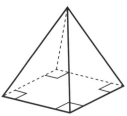

If your answer is yes, draw a sketch to show how.

1 Copy these diagrams onto squared paper and draw enlargements with the given centres and scale factors.

a

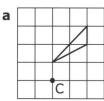

scale factor 2

b

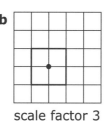

scale factor 3

c

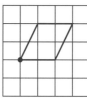

scale factor 3

d

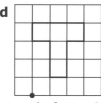

scale factor 2

2 On separate grids draw these enlargements of rectangle R.

   a Enlargement, scale factor 2, centre (0, 0).

   b Enlargement, scale factor 3, centre (1, 1).

   c Enlargement, scale factor 2, centre (0, 3).

   d Enlargement, scale factor 2, centre (1, 2).

   e Enlargement, scale factor 2, centre (⁻1, ⁻1).

   f Enlargement, scale factor 2, centre (3, 4).

   g Enlargement, scale factor 3, centre (2, 2).

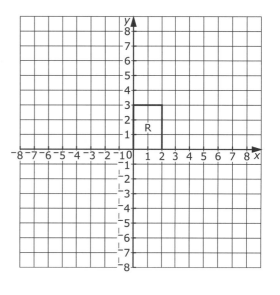

3 Copy these diagrams and find the scale factor and the coordinates of the centre of enlargement in each diagram.

The small shape in each case is the object.

a

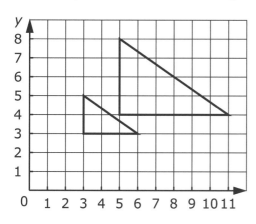

b

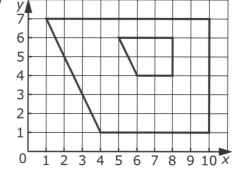

1

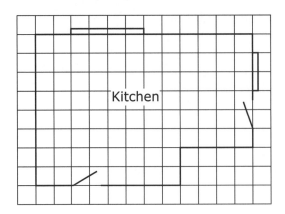

This plan of a school kitchen is drawn to a scale of 0.5 cm to represent 1 m.

a How long is the kitchen?

b What is the maximum width of the kitchen?

c Calculate the number of 50 cm square tiles needed to cover the kitchen floor.

50 cm

50 cm

2 Make an accurate scale drawing of a room in your house, such as your sitting room or kitchen.

Don't forget to show the window, the door and the furniture.

Use a sensible scale.

Remember to write the scale on your drawing.

Level 5

a You can **rotate** triangle **A** onto triangle **B**.

Copy this diagram and put a cross on the **centre of rotation**.

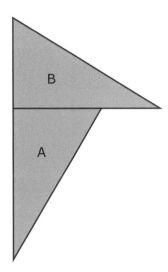

You may use tracing paper to help you. *1 mark*

b You can **rotate** triangle **A** onto triangle **B**.

The rotation is **anti-clockwise**.

What is the **angle** of rotation? *1 mark*

c **Reflect** triangle **A** in the mirror line on a copy of this grid.

You may use a mirror or tracing paper to help you.

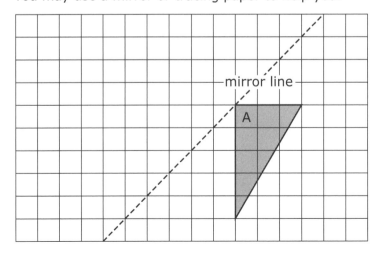

1 mark

Level 6

The grid shows two L-shapes.

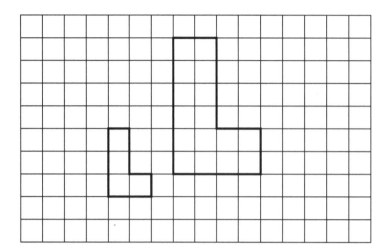

The bigger L-shape is an **enlargement** of the smaller L-shape.

a   What is the **scale factor** of the enlargement?   *1 mark*

b   On a copy of the grid, show where the **centre of enlargement**
       is by marking the correct place with a cross.   *1 mark*

P1.1HW **Making sense of the problem**

For each of these questions, write down what the question is asking
you to find before you solve the problem.

1 **a** A circle has a radius of 12 cm. Calculate its area.

  b Another circle has a circumference of 27 cm.
      Calculate its radius (give your answer to 2 dp).

2 When two numbers are multiplied they give ⁻21 and when added
  together they make 4.
  What are the two numbers?

3 **a** Match each graph to a function.

  i $y = 2x + 3$

  ii $x = 6$

  iii $y = 8$

  iv $y = \dfrac{x}{2} - 2$

  b Does the line $y = 3x + 1$ pass through
      the point (10, 10)?
      Explain your answer.

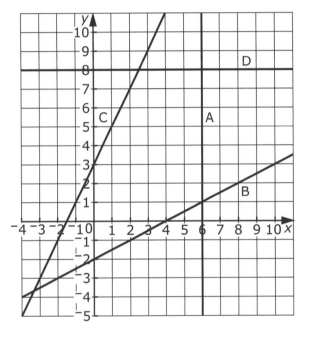

4 Kelvin, Sarah and Hilde are doing their Maths, Science and English exams.

  a Kelvin scored 56% in his Maths exam and 62% in his Science exam. He
      needs a mean score of 60% for the three exams.
      How many marks does he need to score in his English exam?

  b Sarah and Hilde have the same mean score for all three exams. The
      range of Sarah's scores is half that of Hilde's.
      Hilde scored 38% in her English exam, 54% in her Science exam and
      70% in her maths exam.
      Sarah also scored 54% in her Science exam, but got her highest mark
      in English.
      What mark did Sarah get in her Maths exam?

1 This dice has six faces numbered 1 to 6.

Three students collected data on the dice to see if it was biased.
Here are their results.

Student's name	Number of throws	1	2	3	4	5	6
Steph	240	27	54	38	41	60	20
Jon	80	17	8	15	15	5	20
Scott	140	35	15	23	22	12	33

a Which student's data is most likely to give the best estimate of the probability of getting each number on the dice? Explain your answer.

b Collect all the data together and write the results in a table.

c Is the dice biased?
Explain your answer.

d From your data, work out the probability of the dice landing on an odd number.

2 Percy is a pig farmer. He can't remember how many pigs he has so he decides to represent the number of pigs using the letter q.

a Farmer Percy buys 24 more pigs at an auction.
Write an expression for the total number of pigs he has after the auction.

b Farmer Philip has $3q + 18$ pigs.
Farmer Peter has $3(q + 6)$ pigs.
Who has the most pigs, Farmer Philip or Farmer Peter?
Explain your answer.

c Farmer Percy now has the same number of pigs as Farmer Philip.
How many pigs does he have?

1 Karen designs rectangular mirrors.
The length of each mirror is always 5 cm longer than the width.
She decides to make a mirror with an area of 200 cm².
Find the length of the mirror to 1 dp.

2 These patterns are made from matchsticks:

Pattern Number 1 – uses 4 matchsticks

Pattern Number 2 – uses 7 matchsticks

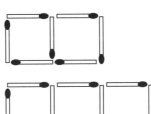

Pattern Number 3 – uses 10 matchsticks

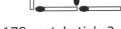

Which pattern number will use exactly 178 matchsticks?

3 Two families buy tickets for the cinema.
The Smart family buy 2 adult and 3 child tickets at a cost of £20.10.
The Chipperfield family buy 4 adult and 2 child tickets at a cost of £26.20.
What is the cost of a child ticket?

4 The area of triangle ABC is 48 m².
List three possible sets of values for a and b.

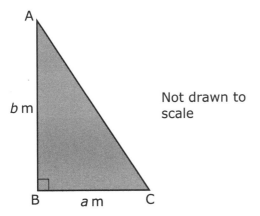

Not drawn to scale

1 At Photoworld prices are reduced in a sale by 10% a day. The sale starts on Tuesday. The sale lasts for three days.

On Monday a camera is priced at £340.

   a John buys the camera on Tuesday.
      How much does he pay for it?

   b Shafaq buys an identical camera on Thursday.
      How much does he pay for it?

2 Sabine owns a restaurant. On Monday she travels 14 miles to buy 13 boxes of wine for £334.62.

The next day she travels to the same place to buy another 10 boxes of the same wine.

How much does it cost to buy the 10 boxes of wine?

3 The ratio of boys to girls in 2 schools is as follows:

     BIG SCHOOL   BOYS : GIRLS = 5 : 7

     SMALL SCHOOL   BOYS : GIRLS = 13 : 16

Which school has the higher proportion of boys?
Explain and justify your answer.

4 **a** KAP industries make an alloy of iron, copper and zinc in the ratio 7 : 4 : 3.
     How much iron is needed to mix with 216 kg of zinc?

   b A type of compost is made in the ratio $2\frac{2}{5}$ parts manure to 3 parts peat.

     How much manure needs to be mixed with 45 kg of peat to make the compost?

Geometric reasoning

1 Calculate the angles marked by the letters *y* and *z* in this diagram.

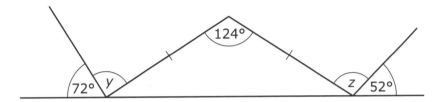

2 Triangles ABC and ACD are both right-angled.

Calculate the angles marked *a* to *f* in this diagram.

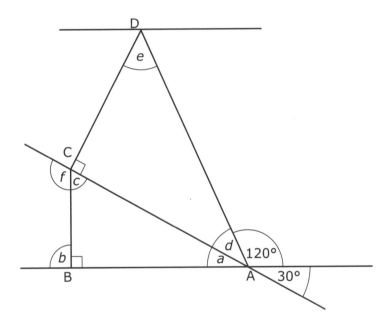

3 Using this diagram, prove that the exterior angle of a triangle (*d*) is equal to the sum of the two interior opposite angles (*a* + *b*).

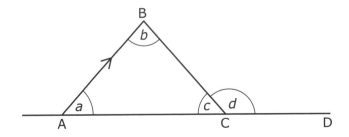

P1.6HW   Checking results

Remember: Check your answers.

1 Simplify these expressions.

    a $4(x - 3) - 3(2 - 4x)$

    b $3k + 7t - k^2 - 3(2t + 1)$

2 Karen and Pete have ordered some tins of paint for their new shop 'Paints-U-Like'.
Each tin contains 5 litres of paint and weighs 3.38 kg.
Each box holds 12 tins.
Each pallet holds 14 boxes.
Karen and Pete ordered 7 pallets.

    a   How many litres of paint did Karen and Pete order?

    b   The lorry delivering the paint can only carry a maximum load of 4 tonnes. Can the lorry deliver all of Karen and Pete's paint in one journey?

3 Jeremy has five cards, each containing a number between 1 and 10.
   ◆   The mean of his cards is 5.
   ◆   The mode of his cards is 8.
   ◆   The range of his cards is 6.
Is this possible? If so, list the numbers on the cards.
Explain and justify your answer.

4 Solve these equations.

    a $4y - 7 = 2y + 3$

    b $6(p + 2) = 12 + 2(12 - p)$

5 Calculate the angles *a* and *b* in this diagram.

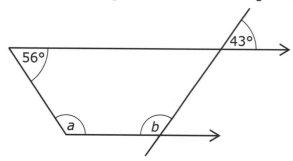

6 Make *r* the subject of the formula $C = 2\pi r$.

Level 5

a I pay **£16.20** to travel to work each week.

I work for **45 weeks** each year.

How much do I pay to travel to work each year?

Show your working. *2 marks*

b I could buy one season ticket that would let me travel for **all 45 weeks**.

It would cost **£630**.

How much is that per week? *1 mark*

Level 6

The information in the box describes three different squares, A, B and C.

> The **area** of square A is **36 cm²**
>
> The **side length** of square B is **36 cm**
>
> The **perimeter** of square C is **36 cm**

Put squares A, B and C in order of size, starting with the smallest.

You **must** show calculations to explain how you work out your answer.

2 marks

Adam has made a number of mistakes in a recent test.

a   Copy his working and circle any mistakes he has made.

b   For any mistakes, write out the correct solution.

1 $3x - 5 = 13$

       $3x = 13 + 5$

         $x = 6$

2 $5x - 12 = 32$

       $5x = 32 - 12$

         $x = 4$

3 $8x + 3 = 4x + 15$

    $8x - 4x = 15 + 3$

       $4x = 18$

         $x = 4.5$

4 $3x + 2 = x + 6$

       $4x = 8$

         $x = 2$

5 $8x - 7 = 5 - 4x$

   $8x + 4x = 5 + 7$

     $12x = 12$

        $x = 1$

6 $2(3x - 1) = 5x$

      $6x - 2 = 5x$

   $6x - 5x = {}^-2$

         $x = {}^-2$

7 $3(2x + 5) = 3(3x - 2)$

      $6x + 5 = 9x - 2$

     $5 - 2 = 9x - 6x$

        $3x = 3$

         $x = 1$

8 $4x - 3 = 2(x + 5)$

   $2x - 1\frac{1}{2} = x + 5$

   $2x - x = 5 + 1\frac{1}{2}$

        $x = 6\frac{1}{2}$

9 $5(2x - 1) + 3x = 6(2x + 1)$

   $10x - 1 + 3x = 12x + 6$

   $13x - 12x = 6 + 1$

         $x = 7$

10 $x^2 - 9 = 0$

       $x^2 = 9$

        $x = 3$

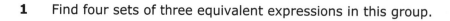

1 Find four sets of three equivalent expressions in this group.

$4x + 12$

$x(4x + 12)$

$6x(2x + 1)$

$2x(2x + 6)$

$2(2x + 6)$

$12(x + 2)$

$4(3x + 6)$

$x(12x + 6)$

$4(x + 3)$

$24 + 12x$

$4x^2 + 12x$

$6x + 12x^2$

2 Given that $6x + 15y = 12$:

  a find the value of

    i $12x + 30y$

    ii $18x + 45y$

    iii $60x + 150y$

    iv $2x + 5y$.

  b write an expression equal in value to:

    i   48

    ii   6.

3 Factorise these expressions.

The first one is started for you.

  a $4x + 2y = 2(\quad)$

  b $3y^2 + 2y =$

  c $14x^2 - 7y =$

  d $3x^3 + 5x^2 - 2x =$

> **Remember:**
> ◆ Take extra care with negative terms.

1 **a** Solve each of these equations.

    i $5(2a - 4) = 3(3a - 4)$

    ii $2(4b + 3) = 2(5b - 10)$

    iii $5(2 - c) = 4(c - 33)$

    iv $2(3d - 4) = 5(d + 3)$

  b A sequence goes a, b, c, d, e ...

    i Substitute the values for a, b, c and d you found in part **a** into this sequence.
What is the value of e?

    ii Write an equation using e (with brackets on each side) that you can solve to get the same value for e as in part **b i**.

2 In an arithmagon the total in the circle is found by adding the rectangles next to it.

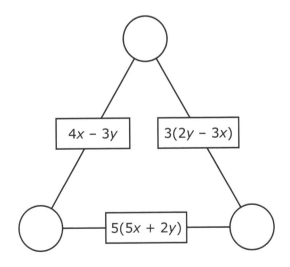

Find the values in the circles if $x = \frac{1}{4}$ and $y = \frac{3}{4}$.

A5.4HW   Algebraic fractions

Remember:

◆ Check your solution in the equation.

1 Match a lowest common multiple with each of the questions. Use this to work out the value of x. The first one is done for you.

a $\dfrac{x}{2} - \dfrac{2x}{5} = 3$ LCM = 10

$\dfrac{10x}{2} - \dfrac{20x}{5} = 30$ multiply by 10 throughout

$5x - 4x = 30$

$x = 30$

Check: $\dfrac{x}{2} - \dfrac{2x}{5} = \dfrac{30}{2} - \dfrac{60}{5} = 15 - 12 = 3$

b $\dfrac{2x}{5} + \dfrac{x}{3} = 11$

c $\dfrac{x}{4} - \dfrac{x}{3} = 14$

d $\dfrac{x}{5} - \dfrac{x}{8} = 3$

e $\dfrac{5x}{6} - \dfrac{2x}{3} = 8$

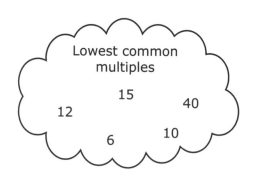

Lowest common multiples

12   15   40   6   10

2 Solve these equations.

a $\dfrac{x-3}{4} = \dfrac{x+2}{9}$

b $\dfrac{3x-2}{10} = \dfrac{x-1}{3}$

c $\dfrac{x+3}{2} = \dfrac{x+9}{4}$

d $\dfrac{2x-4}{5} = \dfrac{x-3}{2}$

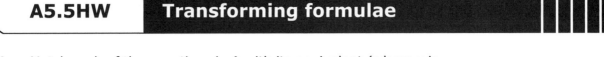
1 Match each of the equations in A with its equivalent (where x is the subject) in B.

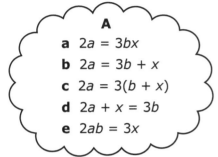

A
a $2a = 3bx$
b $2a = 3b + x$
c $2a = 3(b + x)$
d $2a + x = 3b$
e $2ab = 3x$

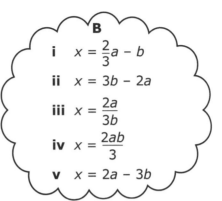

B
i $x = \frac{2}{3}a - b$
ii $x = 3b - 2a$
iii $x = \frac{2a}{3b}$
iv $x = \frac{2ab}{3}$
v $x = 2a - 3b$

2 Make x the subject of each of these formulae.

a $3x + 5 = n$

b $4 + 5x = 2m$

c $T = 3x - 7$

d $P = 6 + 2x$

e $2x + 3s = 4s + x + 5$

f $q = 3rx + 2$

g $a = \frac{x - 2b}{4}$

h $n = axp$

i $s = \frac{2r - 4x}{5}$

j $2p = s - 2n + \frac{4}{3}x$

k $\frac{m}{2} = -4x + \frac{4}{3}b - n$

1 Points A and B are fixed on this coordinate grid and do not move.

When point C is at point (3, 1), ∠ABC is isosceles.

a Point C moves so that the triangle is still isosceles. Write the coordinates of where C could be.

b Point C moves again so that ∠ABC is isosceles and right-angled.
Write down the coordinates of one of the possible new positions of point C.

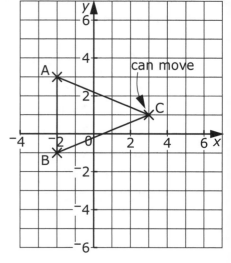

2 **a** Match four of these equations to the lines drawn on the grid.

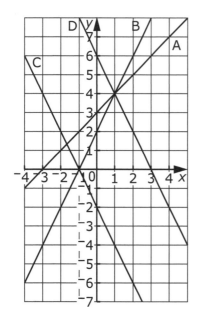

$y = 6 - 2x$
$y = 2x + 2$
$y = x + 3$
$y = 2 - x$
$y = {}^-2x - 2$

b On a similar grid sketch the line of the fifth equation.

106

Level 5

A teacher has a large pile of cards.

An expression for the **total** number of cards is **6n + 8**.

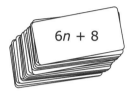

a The teacher puts the cards in two piles.

The number of cards in the first pile is **2n + 3**.

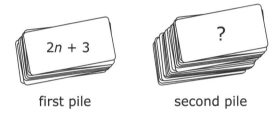

first pile   second pile

Write an expression to show the number of cards in the second pile.   *1 mark*

b The teacher puts all the cards together.

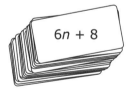

Then he uses them to make **two equal piles**.

Write an expression to show the number of cards in one of the piles.   *1 mark*

continued

Level 5

c   The teacher puts all the cards together again, then he uses them to make two piles.

There are **23** cards in the first pile.

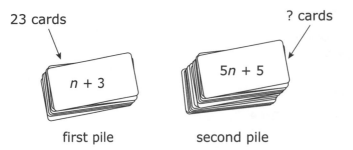

23 cards   ? cards

$n + 3$

$5n + 5$

first pile   second pile

How many cards are in the second pile?
Show your working.   *2 marks*

Level 6

Solve these equations.

Show your working.

$3t + 4 = t + 13$ *2 marks*

$2(3n + 7) = 8$ *1 mark*

This diagram shows the handling data cycle.

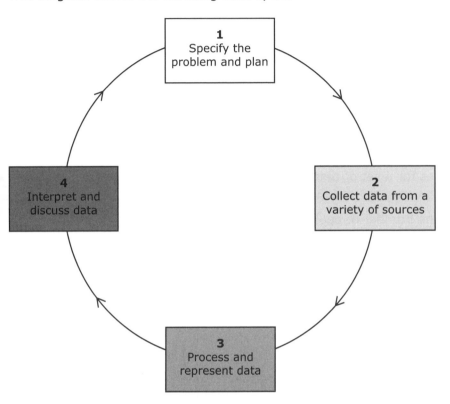

You are at the first stage of the cycle. This stage is very important – it is where you decide on questions that you are going to investigate, and produce a workable plan for how you will go about it.

You should now be able to carry out the tasks explained below.

1 **Write a description of the questions you have decided to investigate.**

   • You should have tried to turn these into specific hypotheses that can be tested.

2 **Write up a plan for your project.**

   • You should explain what data you will need, whether it is primary or secondary data, and how you will obtain it.

   • You will need to explain how the data you describe will enable you to test your hypotheses.

   • You will need to include details about how much data you will be using, and how accurate it needs to be.

1   Describe some sets of data that you have used in your project.
2   Show how you organised the data into tables.
3   Use the descriptions of frequency tables below to help you to explain why you chose to organise the data the way you did.

Here are some types of table that can be used to organise data.

Frequency tables show the frequencies (totals) for different values or classes. They can be used with discrete data, grouped discrete data, or continuous data.

Number of brothers	Frequency
0	5
1	12
2	4
3	1

This table shows the frequencies for a set of **discrete data**.

The frequency column shows the number of people with each number of brothers.

This table shows the frequencies for a set of **grouped discrete data**.
The frequency column shows the number of different-sized litters of kittens.

Number of kittens	Frequency
1–2	1
3–4	5
5–6	9
7–8	1

This table shows the frequencies for a set of **continuous data**, the weights of some diamonds.

The frequency column shows the number of diamonds in each category.

Weight, w grams	Frequency
$0 < w \leq 1$	7
$1 < w \leq 2$	39
$2 < w \leq 3$	108
$3 < w \leq 4$	16

Two-way tables are useful when you make two measurements or observations each time you collect a piece of data.

This table shows the number of T-shirts that a shop has in stock. It shows information about sizes and colours.

	Small	Medium	Large
Red	0	2	8
Blue	7	5	4
Black	3	9	1

The scatter graphs show the scores obtained in the Key Stage 3 Maths, Science and English Tests, by a large number of students.

1   Describe the correlation between the scores obtained in the different subjects.

2   Suggest possible reasons for the relationships.

3   Might a change in one variable cause a change in the other?

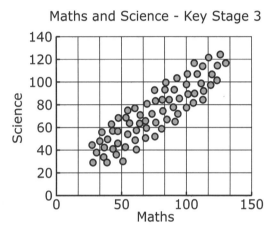

Maths and Science - Key Stage 3

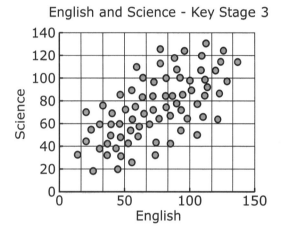

English and Science - Key Stage 3

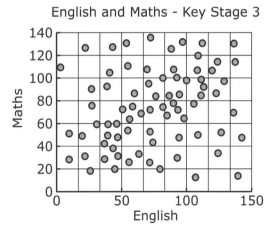

English and Maths - Key Stage 3

Write a set of data that fits each of the descriptions given below.

This set of data has 10 items. The mode is not a very useful measure - because there are three different modes!

A

This set of data has 5 items. The mean, median and mode are all the same.

B

There are 6 items in this set of data. The median is equal to the mode, but the mean is much larger.

C

This is a set of 12 data values. The mode is not a very representative value - it is much smaller than the median and the mean.

D

In this set of data, the mean and the mode are similar, but the median is a lot smaller.

E

For this set of data the mean and the range are quite misleading.

F

Remember:
◆ The mean, median, mode and range are statistics.

A scientist wants to compare the lengths of leaves growing on two different trees.

She measures a set of 30 leaves from each tree.

The results are given in the tables.

The lengths are in centimetres, to 1 decimal place.

Tree A

7.6	6.4	6.6	6.1	7.4	7.6	7.8	5.1	6.3	4.4
8.3	8.1	5.5	7.8	6.0	6.1	8.9	6.9	8.0	7.5
6.6	7.4	8.8	7.5	8.4	7.2	8.4	8.6	6.8	7.1

Tree B

3.6	0.4	3.4	5.6	3.9	3.8	6.4	3.3	7.4	4.3
2.8	3.7	2.9	6.4	4.3	3.6	2.0	2.9	4.1	5.2
1.3	5.8	8.6	3.0	1.5	5.0	4.4	2.3	3.0	1.7

1 Organise the data in suitable tables.

2 Draw frequency diagrams to represent the data.

3 Comment on the shapes of the distributions.

4 Calculate appropriate statistics to represent the data.

5 Use your answers to questions 2–4 to compare the distribution of leaf lengths on the two trees.

Hint: Is the data discrete or continuous?

This diagram shows the handling data cycle.

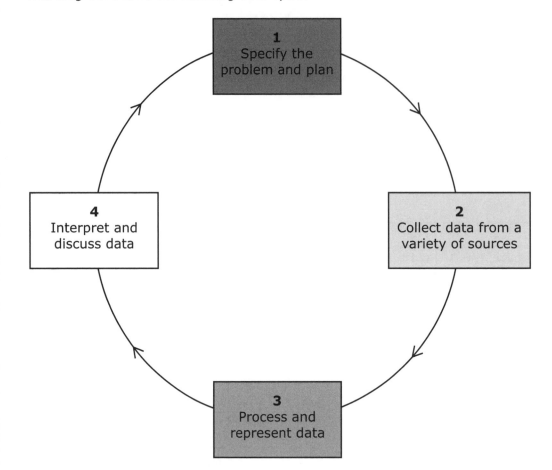

The final stage of your project is where you draw conclusions, and communicate your findings.

*   You need to make sure that your conclusions are justified by the data.

*   You also need to make sure that your conclusions are related to the hypothesis (or hypotheses) that you set out to test at the beginning of the project.

Complete your project by writing up a statistical report.

Include:

*   relevant tables of data, graphs or charts

*   relevant statistics.

Do your conclusions suggest other questions that you could go on to investigate?

Level 5

Some pupils plan a survey to find the most common types of tree in a wood.

Design 1

Instructions

Write down the type of each tree that you see.

For example:

Elm, oak, oak, oak, sycamore, ash, ...

Design 2

Instructions

Use these codes to record the type of each tree that you see.

Ash   A
Birch   B
Elm   E
Oak   O
Sycamore   S

For example:

E, O, O, O, S, A, ...

Design 3

Instructions

Use a tally chart to record the type of each tree that you see.

For example:

Types of tree	Tally
Ash	|
Birch	
Elm	|
Oak	|||
Sycamore	|
Other	

The pupils will only use one design.

a   Choose a design they should **not** use.

Explain why it is not a good design to use.   *1 mark*

b   Choose the design that is the best.

Explain why it is the best.   *1 mark*

Level 6

Two beaches are very similar.

A survey compared the number of animals found in one square metre on each beach.

One beach had not been cleaned. The other beach had been cleaned.

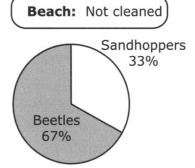

Beach: Not cleaned

Sandhoppers 33%

Beetles 67%

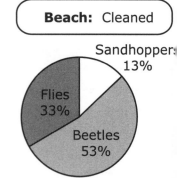

Beach: Cleaned

Sandhoppers 13%

Flies 33%

Beetles 53%

a The data for the beach that had **not been cleaned** represent **1620** animals.

Copy and complete the table to show how many of each animal were found.

Beach: Not cleaned

	Number found
Sandhoppers	
Beetles	
Flies	

2 marks

b The data for the beach that had been **cleaned** represent **15** animals.

Copy and complete the table to show how many of each animal were found.

Beach: Cleaned

	Number found
Sandhoppers	
Beetles	
Flies	

2 marks

c Cleaning the beach changes the numbers of animals and the proportions of animals.

Write a sentence to describe **both** these changes. *1 mark*

1 **a** ABCD is a parallelogram.

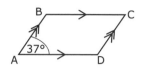

Find ∠ABC.

b ABCD is a rhombus.

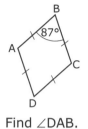

Find ∠DAB.

> Angle sum of a
> quadrilateral = 360°

2 **a** ABCD is a rhombus.

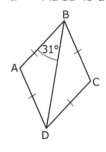

∠ABD = 31°.

Find **i** ∠BAD

　　 ii ∠BCA.

b ABCD is a kite.

Find **i** ∠BCD

　　 ii ∠ADC.

3 **a** These triangles are similar.

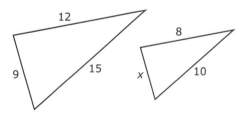

Calculate the length marked x.

b These triangles are congruent.

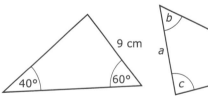

Find the size of:
i side a　　**ii** angle b　　**iii** angle c.

4 **a** Two regular polygons are placed as shown.

Calculate the angle x.

> Interior angle of a polygon = (n − 2) × 180°

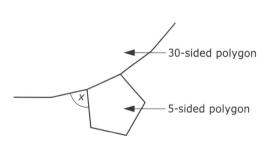

b Investigate the same problem with other regular polygons. What happens to the value of x?

Remember:

◆ The interior angle sum of an *n*-sided polygon is $(n - 2) \times 180°$.

1 Find the angles marked with letters. Give reasons for your answers.

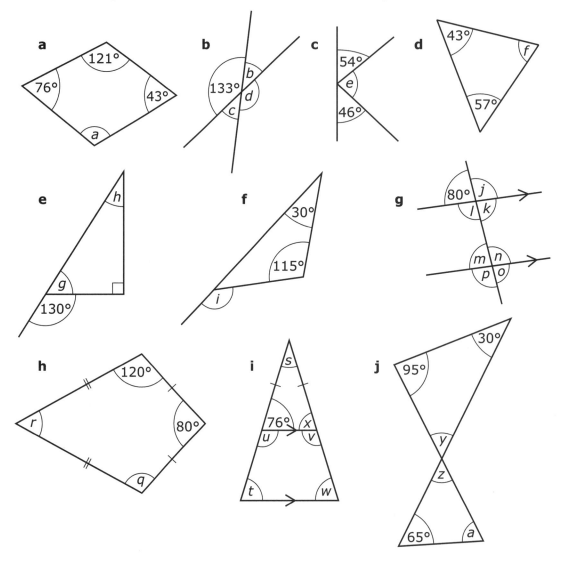

2 Find the sum of the interior angles of these polygons.

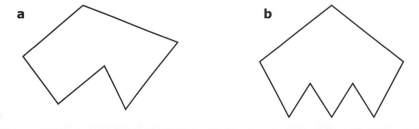

1 Draw these solids on isometric paper:

a a cube of side 3 cm

b a cuboid with sides 3 cm, 2 cm and 5 cm

c a triangular prism of length 4 cm and cross-section of an isosceles triangle of base 4 cm and height 3 cm

d a triangular prism of length 5 cm and cross-section of a right-angled triangle of height 1 cm and hypotenuse 2 cm.

2 These diagrams show the same model from different viewpoints.

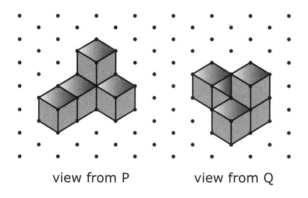

view from P   view from Q

a Add one cube to the model.

   i Draw the view from P

   ii Draw the view from Q.

b Add two cubes to the original model.

   i Draw the view from P

   ii Draw the view from Q.

3 Sketch a model using eight cubes.

Draw **a** the plan view

     b the side elevation

     c the front elevation.

4 Repeat question 3 using ten cubes.

1 **a** On a scale drawing for a new school, the main door measures 5 cm by 12 cm.

The drawing is on a scale of 1 : 25.

Find the actual dimensions of the door.

b Another drawing of the same school is made to a scale of 1 : 50.

Find the size of the door on this drawing.

c A classroom door on one of the drawings measures 4 cm by 10 cm.

Which scale has been used? Explain your answer.

2 Make an accurate scale drawing of your bedroom (or another room in your house).

Remember to include the doors and windows.

3 A model of Frognewton Manor is an exact replica of the actual house using a scale of 1 : 40.

Copy and complete the table.

	Scale model 1 : 40	Actual house
Length of house	120 cm	
Height of house	20 cm	
Length of pool		25 m
Number of cars	6	
Number of windows		37
Length of garden		70 m

1 This map of Notown is drawn to a scale of 1 cm to 50 m.

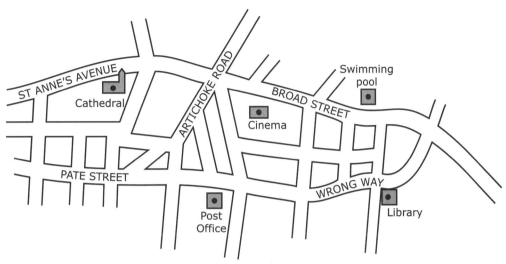

What is the actual distance in metres, as the crow flies, between:

a the cathedral and the cinema

b the cinema and the swimming pool

c the swimming pool and the post office

d the cathedral and the library?

> **Hint:** Measure the distances from the dot at the centre of each landmark.

2 The scale of a map is 1 : 150 000.

Find the actual length in metres of a distance measured as 3 cm on the map.

3 The scale of a map of Scalby village is 1 cm to 50 m.

a The length of the sports field is 127 m.
What length will the sports field be on the map?

b Write the scale of the map in the form 1 : *n*.

> **Hint:** Remember to use the same units for each part of the ratio.

4 Copy and complete this table.

	Map scale	Actual distance	Map distance
a	1 : 500	__ m	6 cm
b	1 : 10 000	3 km	__ cm
c	_____	5 km	5 cm
d	1 : 250 000	46 km	_____
e	1 : 250 000	_____	6.4 cm
f	1 : 20 000	__ km	7.9 cm

1 Find:

   a the volumes

   b the surface areas of these cuboids.

   i

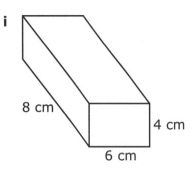

   ii

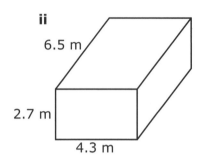

2 Find the volumes of these prisms.

   a

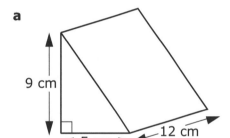

   b

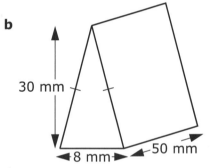

   c

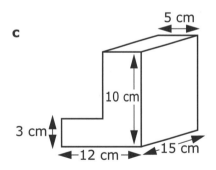

3 Draw and label a diagram of another cuboid with the same surface area as this one.

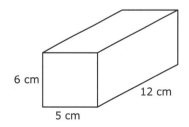

122

I make a model with 6 cubes.
The drawings show my model from **different views**.

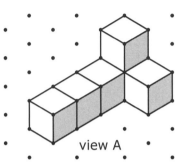

view A

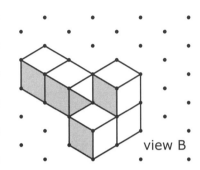

view B

a I join one more cube to my model.
The drawing from **view A** shows where I join the cube.

Copy and complete the drawing from **view B**.
Use isometric paper to help you.

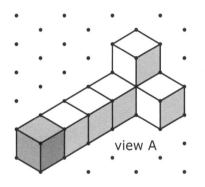

view A

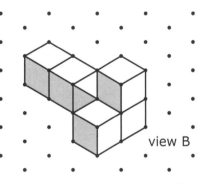

view B

1 mark

b Then I move the cube to a different position.
Copy and complete the drawing from **view B**.

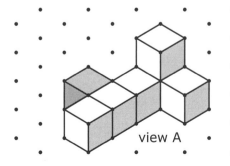

view A

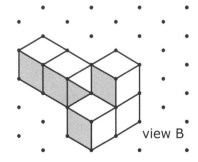

view B

1 mark
continued

Level 5

c I add two cubes to make a different shape.

Copy and complete the drawing from **view B**.

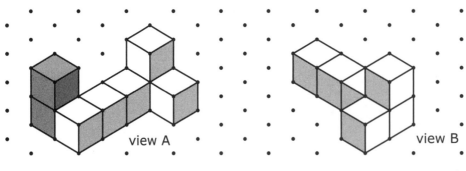

view A   view B

1 mark

d I start again with my original model of 6 cubes.
The drawing shows it from **view A** and from **view B**.
I start to draw it from a different view.

Copy and complete the drawing from **view c**.

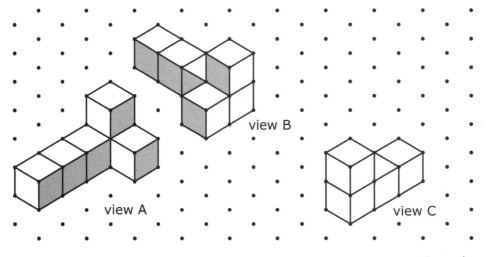

view B

view A   view C

1 mark

Level 6

This door wedge is the shape of a prism.

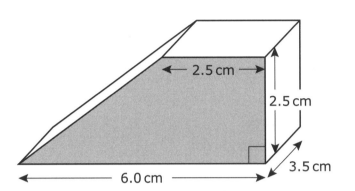

NOT TO
SCALE

a   The shaded face of the door wedge is a trapezium.

Calculate the area of the shaded face.

Show your working.   *2 marks*

b   Calculate the volume of the door wedge.

Show your working.   *1 mark*

> **Remember:**
>
> ◆ Theoretical probability = $\dfrac{\text{number of favourable outcomes}}{\text{total number of outcomes}}$
>
> ◆ Two events are independent if one result does not affect the other.

Maria made these notes about working out theoretical probabilities.

There are various ways to work out theoretical probabilities.

A *When you have a single event with equally likely outcomes, you can just use the <u>formula for theoretical probability</u>.*

B *When you have two events that follow on, again with equally likely outcomes, you can use a <u>sample space diagram</u>.*

C *With two events, you can also find the probability for a particular result <u>by multiplying together the probabilities of the two events</u>. (You can only do this if the probabilities are independent.)*

For each statement A, B and C, give some examples to show how each of the methods is used.

You should be particularly careful to make sure that your examples illustrate the underlined sections in Maria's notes.

Your examples can describe experiments using simple apparatus such as dice or coins, or picking different coloured counters from a bag.

Chris made these notes about the work he had been doing on probability.

- *Mutually exclusive outcomes are outcomes that cannot occur together.*
- *The sum of the probabilities of all the mutually exclusive outcomes of an experiment is always 1.*
- *If two outcomes are mutually exclusive, you can work out the probability of one or the other event happening by adding the probabilities together.*

For each statement A, B and C, give examples to illustrate each of the points.

Your examples can describe experiments using simple apparatus such as dice, coins, spinners, cards or boxes containing different coloured sweets.

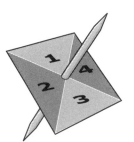

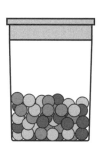

> **Remember:**
> ◆ Write the probabilities on the branches of your tree diagram.
> ◆ Multiply along the branches to find the probability of combined events.

Jake has a pack of red letter cards, and a pack of blue letter cards.

The tables show how many cards there are in each pack.

Red cards

Letter on card	A	B	C	D
Number of cards	4	3	6	7

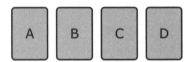

Blue cards

Letter on card	A	B	C	D
Number of cards	3	4	3	10

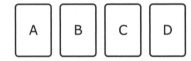

Jake shuffles both packs of cards, then he picks a card from each pack at random.

Hint: Show the choice of colour in the first stage.

1   Draw a two-stage tree diagram to show all the possible outcomes.

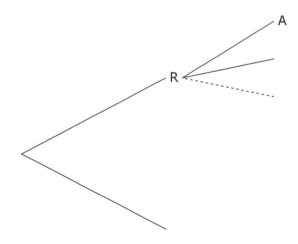

2   Use your tree diagram to work out the probability of each possible outcome.

1 a Draw a tree diagram to show the possible outcomes when a fair coin is tossed three times.

b What is the probability of getting

   i 3 Heads

   ii 2 Heads and 1 Tail (in any order)?

2 Rhian and Tom go to Brighton for a weekend. The weather each day has equal chances of being cloudy, sunny or wet.

a Draw a tree diagram to show the possible weather on Saturday and Sunday.

b What is the probability that Rhian and Tom will enjoy two sunny days?

c What is the probability that there will be at least one wet day?

> **Hint:** First find the probability of one wet day.

3 a Draw a tree diagram to show the possible outcomes when a fair coin is tossed twice.
Use your tree diagram to work out the probability of getting Heads both times.

b Carry out an experiment to estimate the experimental probability of getting two Heads when a coin is tossed twice.
Decide how many trials you need in the experiment.
Calculate the experimental probability of getting two Heads.

c Write a short report explaining how you designed and carried out your experiment.
Give your results and explain whether or not the experimental and theoretical probabilities are in agreement with each other.

In an experiment, two spinners were spun together.

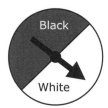 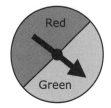

The spinners are not fair – we cannot say that the probability of each outcome is the same.

1   Draw a two-stage tree diagram to show all the possible outcomes when the two spinners are spun together. Do not mark probabilities on the diagram at this stage, because you do not know what they are.

2   The tables shows the results of the experiment.

First spinner	
Black	**White**
60	40

Second spinner	
Red	**Green**
62	38

Out of 100 trials, Black came up 60 times on the first spinner.

We can estimate the probability of getting Black on the first spinner to be $\frac{60}{100}$ = 0.6.

Use the results in the tables to find the probability of getting Black or White, and Green or Red.
Write these on your tree diagram.

3   Now use your tree diagram to find the probability for each combined outcome – for example, the probability of getting Black on the first spinner, and Green on the second one.

4   The table below shows the actual combinations of results that were obtained in the experiment.

	Black	White
Red	38	24
Green	22	16

Explain whether these results agree with the predictions that you made using the tree diagram.

D4.6HW	**Probability experiments**

A bag contains a large (but unknown) number of counters, all of which are blue, green, red or yellow. The probability of picking each colour is estimated. A counter is chosen at random from the bag.

Each trial consists of picking a counter at random, noting the colour, and then returning the counter to the bag.

When the experiment was carried out with just 10 trials, these were the results:

Colour	Blue	Green	Red	Yellow
Frequency	3	3	3	1

1 Work out the probability of getting each colour, based on these results.

The experiment was then continued, until 1000 trials had been carried out. The table below shows the number of times each colour was chosen as the experiment proceeded.

Trials	Blue	Green	Red	Yellow
10	3	3	3	1
20	5	7	6	2
30	7	12	9	2
40	11	15	9	5
50	14	16	13	7
100	22	29	30	19
500	87	144	166	103
1000	163	296	326	215

2 Calculate the experimental probability for each colour at each stage.

3 Write a report about the results of the experiment, describing how the estimated probability for the different colours changed as the experiment went on.

Level 5

A coin has two sides, heads and tails.

heads   tails

a   Chris is going to toss a coin.

What is the **probability** that Chris will get **heads**?

Write your answer as a **fraction**.   *1 mark*

b   Sion is going to toss **2** coins.

Copy and complete the table to show the different results he could get.

First coin	Second coin
heads	heads

1 mark

c   Sion is going to toss **2** coins.

What is the **probability** that he will get **tails** with **both** his coins?

Write your answer as a **fraction**.   *1 mark*

d   Dianne tossed one coin.

She got tails.

Dianne is going to toss another coin.

What is the **probability** that she will get **tails again** with her next coin?

Write your answer as a **fraction**.   *1 mark*

Brightlite company makes light bulbs.

The state of the company's machines can be:

> available for use and being used

or   available for use but not needed

or   broken down.

a The table shows the probabilities of the state of the machines in July 1994.

Write the missing probability.

State of machines: July 1994	Proability
Available for use, being used	
Available for use, not needed	0.09
Broken down	0.03

1 mark

b During another month the probability of a machine being available for use was 0.92.

What was the probability of a machine being broken down?

1 mark

c Brightlite calculated the probabilities of a bulb failing within 1000 hours and within 2000 hours.

Copy and complete the table below to show the probabilities of a bulb still working at 1000 hours and at 2000 hours.

Time	Probability	Still working
At 1000 hours	0.07	
At 2000 hours	0.57	

1 mark

133

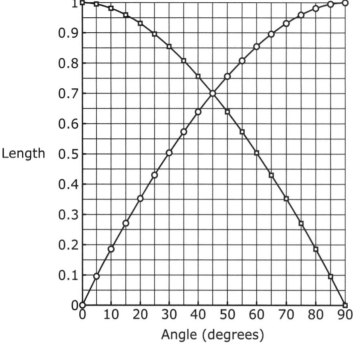

Length

Angle (degrees)

The graph shows the vertical and horizontal lengths of the sides of a right-angled triangle with a hypotenuse of length 1 unit.

The graph shows accurate values of the lengths you measured in B1.1. It covers values of the angle x from 0° to 90°.

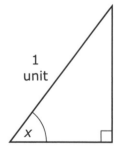

◆ Use the graph to copy and complete this table to show the lengths of the horizontal and vertical sides of the triangle, for angles between 0° and 90°, in steps of 5°.

Angle	0°	5°	10°	15°
Horizontal	1			
Vertical	0			

◆ Why do the two lines cross at x = 45°?
Draw a triangle to support your reasoning.

◆ What do you think would happen if x became more than 90°?
How do you think the graph extends beyond x = 90°?

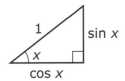

Remember:

When the hypotenuse is 1 unit
- the height of the triangle = sin x
- the base of the triangle = cos x

1 The diagram shows a right-angled triangle. The hypotenuse has length *h*, and the marked angle is *x*.

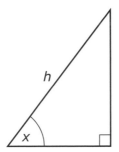

Explain how you can use a scientific calculator to work out the lengths of the other two sides, if you know the values of *h* and *x*. Your explanation should include some examples of the kinds of calculations you could do.

2 Follow your explanations to find the lengths marked with letters in these triangles:

a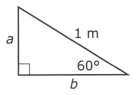

b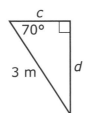

c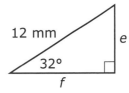

d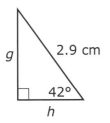

e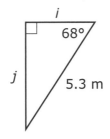

f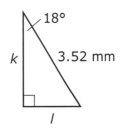

1 Explain how you could use a scientific calculator to calculate the size of the angle *x* in the diagram below, given the lengths of the side *a* and the hypotenuse *h*.

Your explanation should include an example of the type of calculation you would carry out.

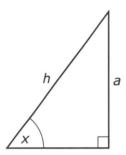

2 Now explain how you could use a scientific calculator to calculate the size of the angle *x* in this diagram, given the lengths of the side *b* and the hypotenuse *h*.

Include an example of the calculation that you would need to carry out.

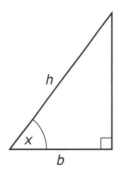

3 Follow your explanations to find these angles:

a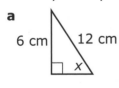
6 cm, 12 cm, *x*

b
62 m, 44 m, *y*, 6 cm

c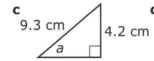
9.3 cm, 4.2 cm, *a*

d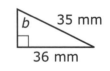
b, 35 mm, 36 mm

e
113 m, *u*, 51 m

f
z, 15.3 cm

g
11.2 m, *i*, 8.9 m

h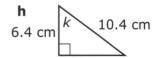
6.4 cm, *k*, 10.4 cm

1 The diagram shows a right-angled triangle. The marked angle is *x*, and the lengths of the sides opposite and adjacent to the angle are *a* and *b*.

Explain how you would work out:

◆ The length *a* if you know the length *b* and the angle *x*.

◆ The length *b* if you know the length *a* and the angle *x*.

◆ The angle *x* if you know the length *a* and the length *b*.

Your explanations should include examples of the type of calculation that you would carry out.

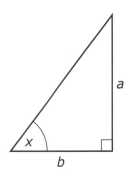

2 Follow your explanations to find these missing lengths.

Give your answers to 1 dp.

a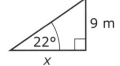

b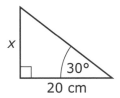

c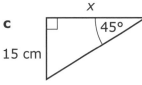

d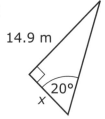

e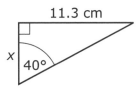

f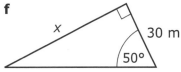

3 Find these missing angles, to 1 dp.

a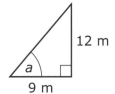

b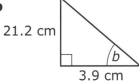

c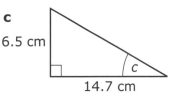

d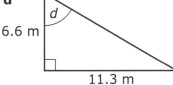

e

f

The diagram shows a right-angled triangle, where the length of the hypotenuse is h, and the lengths of the two shorter sides are a and b.

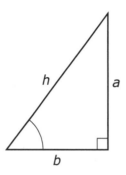

1 Draw the triangle on a square grid.

Draw a square on each side of the triangle so that the side length of the square is equal to the side length of the triangle.

Show Pythagoras' theorem by finding the areas of the squares: $a^2 + b^2 = h^2$

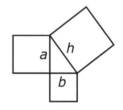

2 Explain how you could use Pythagoras' theorem to work out:

◆ The length of the hypotenuse h, if you know the lengths a and b.

◆ The length of one of the shorter sides (a or b) if you know the lengths of the other two sides.

Your explanation should include examples of the types of calculation that you would need to carry out.

3 Find the missing lengths in these triangles.

Give your answers to 1 dp.

a

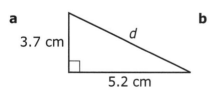

3.7 cm
d
5.2 cm

b

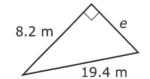

8.2 m
e
19.4 m

c

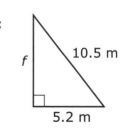

f
10.5 m
5.2 m

Here is a drawing of Castle Cristo, owned by Count Cristo. The Cristo jewels are hidden inside. Frank Pond, international secret agent, is planning to break into the castle to steal the jewels.

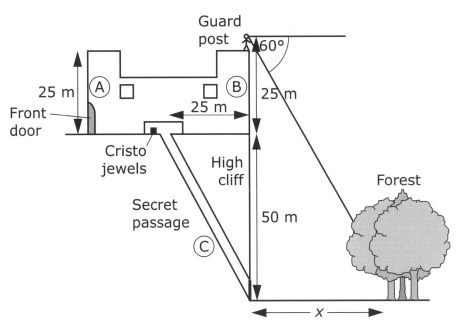

Use a sketch to answer these questions:

Plan A

1   If Frank had a ladder 35 m long, how far from the front door would he have to place the bottom of the ladder to reach the top of wall A?

2   Frank can get to within 10 m of the front door without being seen.
    What is the minimum length of ladder he needs to reach the top of wall A?

Plan B

3   The guard at the top of wall B can only see up to 60° below the horizon. Frank knows that he can just go from the forest to the base of the cliff without being seen. How far away is the forest from the cliff? (Distance marked x.)

4   Frank's ladder is only 35 m long. He has to have at least 10 m between the bottom of the ladder and the base of the cliff. How far can he get up the cliff with his ladder? How far then will he have to climb to reach the top of wall B?

Plan C

5   The secret passage leads from the base of the cliff directly into the jewel room, 25 m inside the castle. Work out the length of the secret passage (C).

Level 7

Ramps help people going into buildings

A ramp that is **10 m long** must not have a **height** greater than **0.83 m**.

a Here are the plans for a ramp:

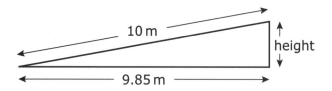

NOT TO SCALE

Is this ramp too high?
You **must** show calculations to explain your answer. *2 marks*

b Here are the plans for a **different** ramp:

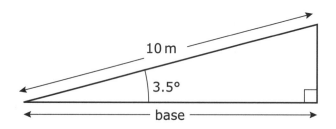

NOT TO SCALE

How long is the base of this ramp?
You **must** show your calculations. *2 marks*

c The recommended gradient of a ramp is 1 in 20.

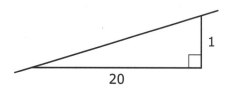

NOT TO SCALE

What angle gives the recommended gradient?
You **must** show your calculations. *2 marks*